Any Fool Can Keep A Secret

Any Fool Can Keep A Secret

JAMES ROBERTSON
Illustrated by Larry

PELHAM BOOKS

First published in Great Britain by
Pelham Books Ltd
27 Wrights Lane
London w8 5tz
1987

British Library Cataloguing in Publication Data
Robertson, James, *1945–*
Any fool can keep a secret.
1. Country life—England—West Country
2. West Country (England)—Social life
and customs
I. Title
942.3'0858'0924   s522.G7

ISBN 0 7207 1771 X

Typeset by Rowland Phototypesetting Ltd
Bury St Edmunds, Suffolk
Printed and bound in Great Britain by
Billings & Sons Ltd, London & Worcester

CONTENTS

Chapter One

The Death of Joy

THE POSTMAN discovered the body of Joy Spontini. It was lying in bed wearing a nightie, teeth in a glass of water, with a peevish expression on its face as if irritated by the abrupt departure of its occupant.

Father Loosemire, the postman, tried to make out that it had been an unpleasant experience, but he fooled none of the customers in the public bar of the Hunted Hind.

The other half of the pub, the lounge bar, had been turned into a masterpiece of macho-rural kitsch – horse brasses, hunting prints, fox masks and an organ which played *Viva España* a great deal during the summer for the benefit of visitors – but the public bar had been left to the aboriginals. The only decoration was a moth-eaten stag's head and a few old photographs of West Country scenes. Here they could gossip, get drunk and spit with no one to mind the dung on their boots.

As usual, a sullen fire smoked in the huge grate, creating a dim irreligious light. The gloom was compounded by the single window's tiny leaded panes and a film of nicotine that coloured glass, lampshades, light bulbs, walls and ceiling a uniform slurry-brown. Only the stupid, the brave or inquisitive anthropologists dared face the stony silence that greeted their entrance for more than one hurried drink.

Father Loosemire had been delivering a final rates demand and a circular about thermal underwear. Middlecott, Joy Spontini's farm, had not been one of the addresses where he was offered glasses of country wine, cups of tea or clutches of doubtful eggs. Nevertheless he had been delivering mail to Middlecott for enough years to know that Joy fed the hens

I

before 6 am, yet there they had been, waiting by the back door at 8, like pensioners outside the post office on a Thursday morning.

'So I knew there was something funny going on,' he told an attentive pub. 'I put my head into the kitchen. "Mrs Spontini!" I shouted. "Are you all right?" Of course, she didn't answer me because she was dead, so I walked in and had a look around. Upstairs was where she was. In her bed, peaceable as a baby.'

Middlecott, which had been in the family for generations, was 150 of the best acres in the parish. Stretching up from the fertile river meadows which still carried the traditional crop of summer weeds – cowslips, orchids, ragged robin and cuckoo flower, it had quickened the blood of dozens of young swains half a century earlier but, at the sight of Joy, their enthusiasm had faltered. Joy had been a big girl, 6 feet 2 inches in her prime, while her moustache had stopped being incipient at the onset of puberty.

Joy had grown to maturity during the Depression when agriculture had been hit as hard as any industry. By the time the war had started, her parents were dead and she was farming the land herself. She had been seriously wooed by the second son of a near-neighbour, but he had dared to investigate her anatomy after a harvest dinner and ended up with a broken arm and jaw. It was not just his injuries that had put off other suitors but also the fact that she had dumped his unconscious body on top of a haystack, 8 feet off the ground, before returning home.

Joy did not seem to mind her lack of lovers. After all, she was stronger than any man in the parish and so had no need for a husband. But she fell just the same when an Italian prisoner of war was billeted on her.

Guido Spontini had been a man of remarkable qualities. He had impregnated Joy within three months of starting work on the farm and married her after six. By the time that Archie Spontini was born – the vet delivered him in the corner of a barn, along with twin calves – there were another two local girls who were well on the way to providing him with siblings.

Joy said little about her husband's behaviour as she was busy with the hay harvest before and after her son's birth, but most of the population of Moorcombe turned up to show their sympathy to her at Guido's funeral after he had been killed by a bull. Nobody asked what he was doing in the bull pen, nor how the bolt on the outside of the door had come to slip across, nor how Joy had come to have human bite marks on her meaty hand. After all, she had been born in the parish and Guido in Rome which was reputed to be even further away than Bristol.

Joy did not associate much with the village after that – not that she had associated much before. She made the community uneasy. It was a bit like having a half-tamed lion, which one avoided whenever possible and took great care not to provoke, living at the bottom of the garden.

Father Loosemire looked round the assembled drinkers, ready to receive questions. He was a small man in his late forties who had fathered four delinquent sons and two daughters. His manner was ingratiating and he had recently covered his thinning head with an acrylic wig as glossy as a horse chestnut. These qualities gave him a certain status in Moorcombe, but he was rarely given such undivided attention as was his at this moment.

The village establishment mulled his information over. It was not quite as rich in detail as they would have liked. They had already heard the news, of course, and had come along to have the bare bones of the event given flesh. Joy's death was the first in the parish for several months and would be worth chewing over on several evenings. But they needed the flesh to chew.

'How did you know she was dead?' asked Kelvin, a farmer who had run the parish like a cockerel in a henhouse until he resigned from the chairmanship of the council in a fit of pique. He was in his sixties and, although he had managed to offload most of his farming duties on to his daughter, Prudence, he still carried around a miasma of dung. Sinister pieces of matter adhered to his spiky grey hair and the stubble on his lantern jaw which was usually thrust belligerently against a world that he knew was out to get him.

'I thought it was a bit funny her just lying there when I opened the bedroom door, so I gave her a poke and she were cold.'

'What did you do then?'

'I went back down to the kitchen to phone the doctor, and made myself a cup of tea and waited till he arrived.'

3

'What's the house like?' asked Kelvin. Very few people had ever been invited through the door.

'Stone sink, water from a pump, lino on the floors where there's not stone flags, tin bath against the wall and a huge sign on the wall saying "Jesus Loves Me". One funny thing, though' – Father Loosemire paused to build up the dramatic tension – 'There was a great big silver teapot under a pile of newspapers in a cupboard in the spare room and a whole heap of silver spoons and forks in a box in the attic. Must have been worth a few bob.'

'Bugger me!' said Kelvin. 'Where did they come from?'

'That wasn't all.' Father Loosemire licked his lips. 'Guess what else?'

'Get on with it!' growled Kelvin.

Father Loosemire looked hurt. 'The cover on her bed had a huge embroidered pistol on it and the initials "JW" with a little heart underneath.'

This was much more than the pub could have expected and it was gratefully received. 'A pistol!' exclaimed the commander in awe. 'How Freudian! She must have had a lover. Whoever he was, he must have been one hell of a chap to have had Joy embroider a pistol.'

The commander was battling bravely against the problems of having a wife who had turned in her headscarf for a woolly hat and a feminist CND badge a couple of years earlier. His Elfrieda would no more embroider a pistol for him than miss a monthly meeting of her consciousness-raising group.

The commander's most distinctive feature was a bushy white moustache which he had grown on retiring from the Navy five years earlier. Having moved to Moorcombe to start a market garden at the bottom of the village, he now found the pub's barley wine considerably more attractive than sprouts on a cold winter's day.

'JW?' ruminated Kelvin, making a sound like a courting grasshopper as he rubbed a calloused hand against his chin. He turned to Jimmy, the village's oldest inhabitant, who, like the Tower of Pisa, continued to defy the logic of decrepitude by flourishing. 'JW? Can you think of a JW?'

Jimmy sat in the Windsor chair that he had occupied by right since the demise of the previous oldest inhabitant five years earlier. Massaging the top of his stick with arthritic hands, he coughed past the hand-rolled cigarette that was always welded to his lower lip. 'There's John Williams. Him that knocks around with your Jason,' he suggested, with a nod at Father Loosemire.

'You silly old bugger!' snorted Kelvin. 'Joy's beard had gone white before John Williams had found out what his balls were for. It must have been an old flame but I'm damned if I can think of a JW.' He shook his head musingly. 'Who'd have thought she would have had a boyfriend? The sly old devil!'

'And there's me, of course,' continued Jimmy. 'I'm JW too: James Albert Wheeler. She could have held a secret torch for me when she was a maid. I was proper popular among the ladies when I was a bit younger.'

Kelvin looked at Jimmy in bafflement. 'You can't mean that Joy fancied you?'

'Why not?' asked Jimmy, his eyes, usually screwed tight against the smoke from his cigarette, widening in indignation. 'There was quite a few that did.'

'There's no accounting for tastes, I grant you. But you wouldn't want to claim Joy.' Kelvin waggled his false teeth in distress at the idea. 'I mean, Joy was like a bear. It would have been awful to have had her after you.'

'I bet I can tell 'ee,' remarked Annie.

Annie, a tiny football-shaped old lady, had buried her husband in the graveyard of the Methodist chapel a mile outside the village a year earlier. Her son had taken over the farm and Annie had retired to a terraced cottage a few doors down from the pub. After a fortnight of baking bread and filling her new larder full of jams and pickles, she had discovered, in quick succession, supermarkets full of delicious white bread and the pub where she was making alarming inroads into her second barrel of sweet sherry that month.

'You sober, Annie?' said Kelvin, looking suspiciously down at her from his bar stool.

Annie cackled. 'You should be able to mind "JW" too, Kelvin. Don't 'ee remember? Back when the fillums used to come to the church hall. *Stagecoach* – that's what it was, and Joy made the vicar run the film again. The vicar got proper cross when she wanted it a third time and so did Joy and it nearly got

5

nasty and her little Archie started to cry and she began to belt him and my Harry had to go for Constable Beech. Joy fell for John Wayne.'

The pub mulled over the picture presented.

'I remember that,' said Jimmy. 'Joy chucked a bench at him.'

'The vicar?' queried the commander.

'No, Constable Beech.'

'Heavens!' said the commander faintly.

'She were a powerful woman, God rest her soul,' said Father Loosemire.

The pub mulled some more and began to cast its mind to the future.

'It's not a bad farm, Middlecott,' said Jimmy. 'I used to be able to take a thousand rabbits a year off it and you have to grow some grass to get rabbits like that.'

'Very damp, down at the bottom,' said Kelvin, shaking his head dubiously. 'And you'd need to spend a fortune on the buildings. They're in terrible shape.'

Bill stirred on his stool. He and Kelvin belonged to the same generation and had known each other since they had smacked their slates over each other's heads in the village school. Like the royal families of Europe, the families in the parish had intertwined down the centuries within and without the prohibited degrees. Kelvin and Bill were nephews, cousins and uncles to each other.

Bill was a small man with a bald head and a long nose that usually had a drip trembling at its end. His ancestral holding was Northcott, just up the river from Middlecott, but he had been more interested in doing deals than farming. He was reputed to be fabulously rich with wads of £50 notes under the trilby that always covered his pate.

Catching the whiff of a scent, he carefully tested the air. 'It's not all bad, Kelvin. It may be a bit rough at the top but there's nothing wrong with that bit of land that runs against your boundary down on the river.'

'Not bad? Not bad? What are you talking about! The river meadow's 24 acres of thistles and rushes. It might have held a thousand rabbits thirty years ago, but they wouldn't find enough to eat there now. It's rubbish! Cost thousands – no, tens of thousands to put it right, what with draining and re-seeding.

And what's the point? With the farming job being so bad these days, you can't make a decent profit anyway. I reckon that land is best left to some up-country mug with more money than sense.'

'Gosh!' said the commander. 'I pity the person who buys it.'

'That's for sure!' said Kelvin, draining his glass and smacking it optimistically down on the counter. Nobody took the hint.

'You might be willing to take it on, though, mightn't you, Kelvin?' asked Bill casually. 'Just to stop it going to rack and ruin, of course.'

Kelvin shook his head decisively. 'No, I wouldn't touch it. Even though it's right on my boundary, I'm not a charitable institution.'

'I don't blame you,' agreed the commander.

'No, I don't either,' said Bill. 'Actually, I was thinking that it would be a real shame to just abandon that bit of land. We do owe a responsibility to future generations. I might take it on myself.'

'How much would you pay?' demanded Kelvin.

'Not a lot. As you said, nobody would want it.'

'That would be really generous of you, Bill,' said the commander. 'You ought to ask someone like the Countryside Commission if they would give you a grant towards buying it.'

'How high would you go?' repeated Kelvin.

'Dunno, really. Up to £1500 perhaps.'

'£1500? It doesn't sound much for 24 acres,' said the commander. 'I might be willing to take it on myself at that price.'

'You'd be buying trouble for yourself if you did,' warned Kelvin, going behind the bar to pour himself some beer. *EastEnders* was on and regulars helped themselves for its duration.

'£1500 an acre, I mean,' corrected Bill, looking innocently down into his glass.

'You bastard!' said Kelvin. 'Shit!' The first exclamation was directed at Bill, the second at his trousers over which he had poured half an inch of beer in his agitation.

'Ho-ho,' said Bill. 'You're all right. I don't want to buy it but Frank Mattock might. He's still trying to build himself an agricultural empire.'

7

'Do you think so?' asked Kelvin anxiously, stuffing a bar towel advertising cider down inside his trousers.

'Funny little thing was Joy's Archie,' said Annie. 'A snivelling little twerp with it, too. A real poor doer. Foreign blood. It don't do to choose a father who ain't from the moor.'

'I'd never heard of Archie,' said the commander. 'What happened to him? I must say I'd never imagined Joy with a husband, let alone a child.'

The commander had lived in the village for only five years but he was already accepted, thanks to the enthusiasm with which he participated in gossip, the most favoured local pastime. His questions gave opportunities to re-hash old tales and scandals which might otherwise have been forgotten.

'We haven't seen Archie for over twenty years,' said Kelvin. 'There was a bit of trouble and he left when he was about sixteen. He was said to have joined the army, isn't that right, Bill?'

Bill nodded.

'What sort of trouble?'

Kelvin adjusted his towel and settled comfortably back on his stool. 'Willie Bladderwick found him in his hayloft with a maid whose parents had a summer cottage. He didn't think anything of it 'cos half the bloody parish used that hayloft in those days. But she went and got pregnant and said that she didn't know how it could have happened since she was still a virgin.' Kelvin shook his head at this example of human folly. 'That story has only worked once in 2000 years, so she then said that Archie had raped her.'

'Heavens!' murmured the commander. 'What a monstrous child!'

'He was a bit of a bad lot, Archie,' agreed Kelvin. 'They said he did a bit of rick burning and he certainly nicked diesel from a tank I used to have up by the road. Anyway, Constable Beech let him think there might be trouble about the girl and he scarpered. Good bloody riddance! That's what we all thought.'

'Heavens!' repeated the commander. 'What a sordid little story! But what was so special about Willie Bladderwick's hayloft?'

'He didn't make his hay into bales,' explained Kelvin. 'It was loose like it was in the old days. Willie'd 've died a rich man if he'd had £1 for every maid who went up the aisle with a full belly on her 'cos of a bit of jiggery-pokery in his hayloft.'

'Frank Mattock was caught that way,' said Jimmy.

'So was I,' said Father Loosemire gloomily. 'Although I'm blowed if I remember why we went to Willie's barn. There were ricks in every field in those days.'

'Sow thistles,' contributed Annie. 'Put you right off courting, getting sow thistles in your arse. Bladderwicks never had no sow thistles in their top fields. All the girls used to know that. Old-fashioned meadow grass hay it was too. None of that nasty spiky cocksfoot.' The bench beneath her creaked as her haunches shifted with reminiscent pain. 'I'll tell you one thing. Joy'll have left the farm to Archie, if he's not come to a bad end by now. He'll be back, mark my words. He might even be down for the funeral.'

'She's right!' exclaimed Kelvin. 'I never thought of that. Bloody Archie Spontini back in Moorcombe. Cor! That'll be trouble, mark my words!'

Marking his words, the pub mulled some more.

Moorcombe farms came in two varieties. Along the river valley below the village, they were fertile and sometimes flat, the fields dotted with dairy cows. As the land climbed the wooded hillside up to the moor itself where the weather wuthered away for most of the year, they grew bracken, heather, sheep and miserable bullocks, their backs hunched against the driving rain.

Kelvin's farm, Southcott, flanked the river just downstream of the village. Then came Middlecott and, finally, Bill at Northcott on the parish boundary. Beyond that was the beginning of 'up country', which covered the United Kingdom east and north of the county of Somerset.

When the tom-toms confirmed that Archie was indeed the heir, Kelvin put Prudence to work laying the hedge that obscured his vision of the first 100 yards of the Middlecott lane. He wanted to be quite certain that Archie's arrival would not be missed.

Kelvin came out to ensure that she did a decent job. He also came to get a new stick, having broken his last one on the backside of a bullock. He liked to take 4 feet of stout blackthorn to market with him so that, while leaning on the rails round the sale he could jab the beasts judiciously as they trotted past.

He was caressing a promisingly knobbly candidate when a Mini pick-up turned into the lane. It stopped opposite Prudence. Pushing open the window, Bill looked up the hedgebank where Prudence was wrestling with an iron bedstead blocking a gap.

'Morning, Prudence.'

The elderly collie that was sitting amid a tangle of stakes and baler twine in the back of the truck thumped its tail in agreement.

A smile writhed across Prudence's lips.

She was entering her prime. It was unfortunate that her prime had come along a couple of decades after everyone else's. As Kelvin's only child, she had been put to work after her mother had fled to Abraham's breast for refuge. She had naturally been expected to play a prominent role when her generation came to make the marital alliances setting the pattern of land ownership for the future. But even the most ambitious younger sons had quailed before the prospect of a father-in-law such as Kelvin and the possibility, however remote, that his mousy daughter might have inherited any of his characteristics.

The fate of Guido Spontini had been a terrible warning to local fortune hunters.

Prudence had not seemed to mind. She rarely left the farm and, when she did, she said so little that nobody would have known if she had minded. It was therefore all the more surprising when she permed her lank brown hair, cut the size of her army surplus sweaters and jeans to bring out her best characteristics and developed a line in bone-dry humour which she directed at her unnoticing father.

'Morning Bill,' replied Prudence, moving aside to make room for Kelvin in the hedge gap as he came hurrying across.

'Where do you think you're going, Bill?' he asked, scrutinizing the back of the vehicle for clues.

Bill smiled. It was the smile of the child that knew what lay inside the birthday parcel. 'To look at Joy's cattle.'

'Why?' asked Kelvin, uneasily aware of the quality of the smile. 'What've they got to do with you?'

'The solicitor's asked me to buy them for what I think they're worth because Archie won't be coming down for a couple of weeks and wanted rid of them.'

'Christ! At your own valuation! No wonder you're looking as if you've found a shilling! Why didn't he ask me? Bloody cheek! I'm right next door.'

'The solicitor knows you, Dad,' said Prudence.

'That's exactly what I mean. Huh! I told that useless bastard that he ought to learn to do his job five years ago. He's obviously taken no notice.' Kelvin's snort of contempt was as thunderous as an elephant's fart. 'Anyway, where do you think you're going to keep them? You won't get much of a price if you sell them at the moment. I'll rent you some grazing if you like, but it's not cheap at this time of year. Not if you want a bit of grass.'

Bill smiled again. Opening the door of the vehicle, he stepped out on to the lane. Here it marked the boundary between Middlecott and Kelvin's farm, Southcott.

It was spring and the hedgerow trees still etched their bare branches against the grey sky. Fifty yards away the lane rose to cross the river over a narrow hump-backed stone bridge, built for the pack-horse rather than wheels. Large vehicles had to approach the farm across a ford beside the bridge. The river's habit of rising a couple of feet whenever a shower of rain crossed its birthplace up on the moor had helped preserve Middlecott from the prosperity created by lorryloads of fertilizers, cattle cake and daily visits from the milk tanker. The farm had changed little in fifty years.

Stepping over a large pothole, Bill stood at the base of the 6-foot hedgebank and looked up at Kelvin.

The latter stared suspiciously down over the top of the bedstead. 'Well? There won't be anywhere else. Everyone's holding on for next month's grass sales.'

Bill's smile grew even wider. 'It's very kind of you, Kelvin. But I'm all right. I've got the grazing here on Middlecott for the summer.'

'Christ!' repeated Kelvin, shaking the bedstead like a trapped gorilla, showering rust and twigs at Bill's feet. 'I should have had that.'

'You should've asked,' said Bill.

'I didn't know!' cried Kelvin. 'I could have cleaned up, stocking it with sheep.'

'I didn't know till I asked,' said Bill with a wink towards Prudence.

'How much are you paying?'

'It's a very fair deal, Kelvin. Very fair.' Bill nodded his head sagely, his brow furrowing with sincerity beneath the brim of his hat.

'How much?' repeated Kelvin through gritted dentures.

'£20.'

'£20 an acre! That's robbery! You haven't got it for the whole season for only £20 an acre?'

'Not exactly.'

Had Kelvin been a wolf, he would have howled his frustration to the leaden sky. As he was human, he could manage only a strangled roar. 'Aargh! Tell me, you bastard. How much are you paying?'

Bill weighed up Kelvin through narrowed eyes. Satisfied that he had wound him up as far as he would go, he delicately disengaged the ratchet.

'Oh, I'm not paying anything. They're paying *me* £20 a week to keep the grass under control. I'll be using my new cattle.'

Touched the brim of his hat at Prudence, Bill returned to his vehicle and buzzed on up the lane.

The heir did not make Joy's funeral. She was laid in the churchyard surrounded by scores of her ancestors whose headstones frowned down upon the 6-inch lead cross that marked the grave of her husband.

Present to mark her passing was the establishment of Moorcombe. It retired to the pub opposite when the weight of soil on top of her coffin was sufficient to ensure that her earthly remains would stay put for eternity. It had hardly time to down the first round of drinks before Father Loosemire bustled into the pub with more news.

'You could have knocked me down with a feather,' he said. 'I was in the post office, sorting a card from the Seychelles for the squire. Pretty place it looks. It was from his daughter who's on holiday, the one . . .'

'Get on with it,' said Kelvin.

'Anyway, this red Range Rover pulled up and one of them chocolate-box countrymen got out – all tweed and green wellies. It took me a minute but I recognized him. It was Archie Spontini! He had his father's blue eyes and black hair but that chin of the Chilcotts. Comes out like the white face on a Hereford cross bullock, it does. "You're Archie," I said. "That's right," he said. And it was!'

'How old was it?' asked Kelvin.

'This year's,' replied Father Loosemire. 'D registration.'

There was a respectful silence.

'What does a new one of those cost?' asked Jimmy.

'Lots,' said the commander.

'I don't much like the sound of that,' said Kelvin. 'If he's got lots of money, he may not be so keen to sell the land. How long's he down here for?'

'I didn't ask.'

Kelvin looked at Father Loosemire in astonishment.

'It wasn't my fault!' he protested. 'I'd just told him where Middlecott was and the telephone rang. He was out the door before I could stop him.'

'Huh! And when was that?'

'About half an hour ago.'

Kelvin thought for a few seconds. 'Was he in such a hurry because he'd nicked something?'

'I don't think so. Why, should he have?'

'Remember what he was like before, always nicking things. Blood will out. There's foreign blood in Archie Spontini and we all know what that means!'

'Do tell,' said the commander.

'Hitler. He was a foreigner. And that new bald Russian bloke. He's foreign too.'

'Don't be so stupid, Kelvin!' said Jimmy. He had stayed with his son in Canada a couple of years earlier and now was an authority on international affairs. 'Virtually everybody in the world's a foreigner.'

'Just proves my point. Look at the mess the world's in. You can never trust a foreigner.'

'Can you not trust me?' said a husky voice.

Kelvin had been so vehement in his xenophobia that he had

not noticed Helga, the licensee, come through from the lounge bar.

'I too am foreign, Kelvin.' Helga's voice, like her looks, was Garbo at her most erotic.

Kelvin gasped in dismay. Within the Stygian darkness of his soul, his guardian angel furiously fanned the flickering spark of light which was his slavish adoration of Helga. 'I didn't mean you, Helga. You're not foreign. You're an English publican and there's nothing less foreign than that.'

'A beefeater,' suggested Jimmy. 'One of them's more English than a publican.'

''Cept a beefeater, I suppose,' agreed Kelvin. 'But there aren't many of them about.'

'But I was born a Romanian.'

'It weren't your fault that you were born there. And that was a long time ago.'

'Kelvin! You should never make remarks like that about a lady's age.'

'Aah!' groaned the guilty one, smiting himself on the brow. The rest of the bar looked on with concern as his sleeve jogged his glass, spilling some beer. 'I didn't mean that, Helga. It wasn't a long time ago at all.'

Kelvin was still waving his arms around to show his remorse, so the commander leaned over to remove his glass from further danger. The audience relaxed. It would have spoiled their enjoyment of Kelvin's discomfiture had they been distracted by potential wastage of beer.

'I know you didn't mean it, Kelvin,' said Helga. 'I think you are very sweet. If you'll excuse me, I must change a barrel.'

Kelvin blushed. She patted him on the cheek and left the bar. But the pub was not going to let him off the hook that easily.

'That was downright insulting, Kelvin,' accused Bill.

There were enthusiastic murmurs of support.

'Quite,' agreed the commander.

'You're no gentleman, Kelvin,' said Annie from her bench.

'Yeah,' added Jimmy.

Kelvin looked round like a badger cornered by terriers. 'I'm sorry,' he said humbly.

Now that the pub had got Kelvin where it wanted him, it did not quite know what to do with him next. It could have tried to extract drinks but Kelvin had lost a toe in 1965 in an attempt to kick a 10 shilling note out of the path of a finger bar mower. However, it was saved from its quandary by a thump on the door. Only strangers tried to push through before lifting the latch. The entire pub turned to stare at this *Deus ex machina* as the hollow click of the latch rang through the room and the door creaked open.

The quondam apple of Joy's eye, unmistakable in a black-and-white tweed jacket with 2-inch checks, hairy tie, cavalry twills and expensive-looking brown brogue shoes, walked delicately towards the bar. The patrons parted to let him through. He was in his early forties, slightly overweight, with a round face and eyes like a whipped spaniel.

Kelvin looked him carefully up and down and sniffed.

Glancing along the bar, the newcomer gave a nervous laugh. 'Is it do-it-yourself, then, squire?'

'Only if you're a regular,' replied Kelvin.

'Oh well, I soon will be.' Archie went round the bar to pour himself a drink.

Kelvin, slumped over his beer, slowly straightened, his eyes gleaming. He cleared his throat loudly.

'Would you like a drink?' said Archie, catching a hint as subtle as a nuclear bomb.

'Well, that's very civil of you. I don't mind if I do. You're a more generous man than your mother.'

'Oh, you know who I am?'

'Know you? Know you? Of course I know you. I'm Kelvin. We're blood.'

The precise degree of relationship would have been impossible to establish. But the natives had a sense of family akin to that of the Pharaohs, and in Moorcombe a native was one who did not know when or if his ancestors had ever lived more than 2 miles beyond the parish boundary.

'Are we?' said Archie. 'I don't remember having any relations.' He examined Kelvin with a critical eye. Given a choice, few would have selected Kelvin for the role of long-lost relative. 'I'm charmed, I'm sure,' said Archie, a notable lack of enthusiasm in his voice. 'You knew my mother? I'm down to look over the farm. I'm her heir.'

'I know. It's a great tragedy. We've just buried her.'

'Yes. I was sorry to miss the funeral, but I was seeing the solicitor.' He sighed. 'Yes, it comes to us all. The grim reaper. It's very sad. It means that I'm an orphan.'

'So am I,' quavered Jimmy.

'Oh, what a shame!' said Archie.

Kelvin shook his head to dispel the picture of Jimmy's quindecimarian parents, had they been spared. 'I'm Kelvin Morchard who lives next door. I can remember you as a little boy.'

'Little boy! Did you really? It all seems so long ago. I can remember spending all my time in the woods and fields. Real child of nature, I was. I used to love all the wildlife – the birds and the flowers and things like that. There were some lovely yellow flowers. What were they?' Archie's brow knitted for a moment in the strain of recall. 'Dandelions!' he said, triumphant. 'That's what they are called. Are there still dandelions? I haven't thought about dandelions for years and years and years.'

'That sounds like a long time,' said the commander politely.

'Oh, yes. It is a long time, squire. I've been too busy in my life to think about dandelions down the years.'

'Oh? And what were you busy at?' asked the commander, thinking about the D-registration Range Rover.

'Making money. I've got retirement homes all along the South Coast.'

There was a respectful pause.

'And did you make a lot of money?' asked Kelvin.

'Can't grumble, squire. It's not so hard these days. You know what they say.'

Another pause.

'What do they say?' asked Kelvin.

'You know. It's the first million that's the hardest.'

Kelvin coughed into his beer and put the glass back on the counter. 'You must get it from your father,' he said, voicing the astonishment felt by all the natives that anyone who had grown from the seed of Joy could make such a remark.

Its truth was a separate issue.

'Coo!' said Jimmy, pushing his glass across the bar. 'No wonder you can afford a new Range Rover! I'll have a large whisky.'

Chairs scraped and glasses clinked as the pub realized that it had on its hands a phenomenon which might well yield a considerable quantity of free liquor.

The round came to £12.35. The returning prodigal placed two fivers and three £1 coins into the open till, shutting it without taking his change. A sigh ran round the room.

After a proprietory gulp of his new pint, Kelvin wiped his mouth on his sleeve. 'You'll be selling the farm and going back to London to make more millions, then?'

'I haven't decided yet.'

'But your business. It'll need looking after.'

'No. I was thinking it was time I sold out. Mother's death couldn't have come at a more convenient moment. I've got plenty of time on my hands and I thought I might try to make something of the place.'

'Oh?' said Kelvin. 'Make something of the place? I wouldn't advise you to get involved in farming at this stage of the game.'

He shook his head sagely. 'No. Farming's no business for an amateur these days. You'll lose your shirt. And that farm of yours ain't no bloody good. You must have seen the state it's in.'

'There's nothing wrong with it that a bit of money won't put right,' replied Archie. 'Just the ticket for me at the moment. I thought I'd do this organic lark. I nearly got into wholefoods once myself and there's big money there.'

'Organic?'

'Yes. Free-range chickens and eggs and vegetables and things.'

'Market gardening?' bristled the commander, who was a market gardener.

'Oh no, squire. Proper farming. I thought a few hundred acres would be right. No half-measures for me!'

'What are you talking about!' exclaimed Kelvin. 'The whole bloody farm's only 150 acres!'

'Is it? Well, I could always get a bit more land.'

'Jesus!' Kelvin slumped back on his stool. A thought popped into his head. 'Are you married?'

'Not at the moment,' replied Archie. 'What's the talent like round here? Is this village as dead as I think it is?'

'Well,' said Kelvin, 'there's always Prudence.'

'There's Chastity Trotter too,' suggested Jimmy, draining his glass. 'She's been cycling over from Brockford every other Thursday for twenty-five years, now. She's the hoor. I think she's got a vacancy at the moment. I'll recommend you to her if you buy me another drink.'

'It's very kind of you but I really must go,' replied Archie hurriedly – so hurriedly that, deserting his gin and tonic, he edged round the bar towards the door. 'I've got quite a lot to do.'

'Well!' said Kelvin as the door slammed behind Archie, sending a great puffball of smoke towards the ceiling from the fire. 'What do you make of that?'

'Joy once got a letter from the Seaview Rest Home in Brighton,' said Father Loosemire. 'He might be telling the truth.'

'He's not quite what I was expecting,' said Jimmy.

'Little shit, if you ask me,' said the commander.

'That bugger's going to be trouble, mark my words,' said Annie. 'I'm not surprised he says he's forgotten what it was like here. He were a right little bugger when he was a kid and he still is. Imagine seeing a solicitor when your own mother's being put in her grave.'

'A rich little bugger, though,' said Kelvin.

'Ah! But it'll be all froth. He'll just have paper. Not real money,' said Annie.

'I'm quite happy with paper money,' said Kelvin. 'And, of course, he's got the farm. And he's just the right age for Prudence.'

The pub, and with it the village, had a great deal to think about.

Chapter Two

Bird Table

'IT'S BORING, being old,' quavered Jimmy.

'It's better than the alternative,' said the commander.

Jimmy grunted doubtfully. Tomorrow would be pension day and he often had to nurse a half-pint for much of Wednesday evening. This was depressing.

'You need a hobby, Jimmy,' said Lindy. 'It doesn't do a man of your age any good to hang around pubs drinking the whole time.'

Lindy was the district nurse, a small brisk woman in her late thirties with short dark hair. She would have been a beautifully proportioned Amazon at 6 feet, but at 5 the proportions were less satisfactory.

'That's the trouble,' said Jimmy. 'I may go into pubs, but I don't always drink.'

'I bought you a pint when I came in,' said the commander.

'That was two hours ago, but I'm not complaining,' complained Jimmy.

'Yes you are,' said Kelvin. 'You need a hobby, like Lindy says. Go and watch the television on Wednesdays and then you won't bore all of us as well as yourself.'

'That's very cruel, saying I'm boring,' said Jimmy.

'It's your fault. You said it,' replied Kelvin.

The pub sat in silence for a couple of minutes, the only sounds being the measured tick from the circular clock on the wall opposite the stag's head and the hiss of the resentful fire. Jimmy peered through the smoke of his cigarette, but nobody looked likely to buy. He sighed a deep sigh of sadness.

'She's right, you know,' said Ivor, a dairy farmer in his fifties with a cow-lick of grey hair. He had lived in the parish for only twenty-five years but his qualities of diplomacy and the fact that he was educated and a gentleman, albeit a very thin and small gentleman, had elected him chairman of the parish council in Kelvin's place. His sense of humour was that of a smutty twelve-year-old.

'Who's right?' asked the commander.

'Lindy. Jimmy needs an interest.'

'We've already discussed that,' replied the commander. 'If you remember, Kelvin recommended television.'

'Don't be silly, that's not a hobby. I'm serious. I think everybody should have a hobby.'

'What's yours?' asked Kelvin.

'Well . . . er . . . shooting and fishing, I suppose, and I do the commentating at gymkhanas.'

'I still go shooting,' said Jimmy.

'You ought to have put away your gun for good after you shot that pheasant-that-wasn't in February,' said Ivor.

'What's a pheasant-that-wasn't?' asked Lindy.

'A chicken.'

'It wasn't my fault,' said Jimmy.

'Don't be absurd!' said Kelvin. 'Of course it was your fault! Whose else could it have been?'

'I can't help it if I'm a senior citizen and my eyes aren't what they were,' whined Jimmy.

'Huh!' grunted Kelvin. 'You doddering old fool! The trouble is that you and your gun are liable to take away the chance of some other poor sod becoming a senior citizen.'

'Quite right, Kelvin,' said Ivor. 'There can be no doubt that it's time Jimmy put his gun away for good and took up some other interest. Something more appropriate for a man of his years. What is it that old folks get up to in these centres? Making raffia mats or playing bingo while some jolly lady leads you in a sing-song. Wonderful fun!'

Jimmy shuddered. 'I don't fancy that sort of thing. It doesn't seem natural. Not like shooting and hunting and fishing and ferreting and coursing.'

'Take up bird watching,' suggested Lindy.

'Bird watching? What'd I want to do that for? Mind you, I could start collecting eggs again, I suppose. I used to do that seventy years ago.'

'That's against the law now,' said Ivor.

Jimmy was not listening. His brain cells were rumbling into a reminiscence. 'I got a honey buzzard's egg once and sold it to the old squire's father. He always wanted a kite's egg, but I never got one. Didn't ever see a kite, now I think on it. Silly name for a bird, though. Did you know there was a kind of tiger in South America that's called a jaguar? Imagine calling an animal after a car! Kite always seemed a bit like that too. They say there used to be kites down here but it rains more than it used to and they can't stand the winters no more. I can't either. Plays up my joints like anything.'

'I had siskins all last winter,' said Stephanie from the bench beside Annie.

A silence followed this announcement. Stephanie was not a regular evening visitor to the pub as it clashed with her exercise programme. She and her husband, Malcolm, were English lecturers at the college of further education a dozen miles away. They lived in a cottage known locally as 'The Swallow's Nest' as its owners came and went like migrating birds.

Stephanie and Malcolm had already lived there for the past three years, the longest tenure since 1949. She believed that if she were fit she would enjoy life more, so virtually all her leisure hours were spent in jogging, badminton and aerobics. This left her very little spare life to enjoy.

Not that the village minded, since one of Moorcombe's notable sights was Stephanie in her running shorts, breasts bouncing inside her singlet, as she pounded the country lanes. Often Malcolm would be beside her in an orange tracksuit, monitoring which of his neighbours had eyes which bulged with lust as his wife passed.

'Siskins?' probed the commander delicately.

'Yes, four of them. They didn't get on with my tits.'

The trend in the conversation should have prevented any ambiguity, but Ivor would have picked up any *double entendre*, even in his own death sentence. 'You have great tits, Stephanie.'

'I did have, but I'm afraid I might lose them.'

Ivor hugged himself with glee but the natives were shocked. Overt reference to sexual matters was one of the village's few conversational taboos.

Kelvin studied Stephanie's chest out of the corner of his eye and cleared his throat uneasily. 'Late spring again.'

'Yes,' said Bill, picking up the cue. 'It's the east wind. Killer, the east wind, at this time of year. Comes all the way from Russia, they say.'

'It brings me siskins,' said Stephanie.

This led to another pause during which the aboriginals examined the beer mats on the bar in front of them with knitted brows.

Jimmy leaned forward on his chair. 'What exactly is siskins?' he whispered hoarsely to the commander.

The commander blew through his moustache, embarrassed. 'Not exactly sure,' he muttered. 'It sounds jolly peculiar. I suppose it must be one of those female complaints like thrush.'

'Thrush?' queried Jimmy, forgetting the need for discretion.

'Thrush? Have you got thrush, commander?' asked Stephanie.

The commander turned crimson. 'How dare you!'

23

Stephanie, understandably, looked bewildered. She turned to Lindy, who was close by. 'What did I say?'

Lindy shrugged 'Search me! What's wrong, Commander?'

'I really don't think we should talk about such things,' said the commander, still upset. 'Ivor, it's not a laughing matter.'

Ivor, his handkerchief out, was dabbing his eyes.

'What I mean,' the commander continued, 'is that some things are just best left unsaid.'

'What's wrong with talking about a tit, or thrush or siskins?' demanded Stephanie. 'It's not as boring as most of the conversations in here, but I don't see that's any reason to get cross about it.'

'For heaven's sake!' exclaimed the commander. 'Watch what you're saying.'

'Tits?' essayed Stephanie. 'Great tits?'

He flinched.

'Thrush?'

He frowned.

'Siskins?'

He spoke. Angrily. 'Look, Stephanie, vulgarity for its own sake simply isn't funny. I'm disappointed in you.' He turned to Ivor. 'And I can say exactly the same to you. Pull yourself together, man!'

Ivor had made the disastrous error of supping some beer during the last exchange, and he was now in some difficulty as he sprayed bitter from an assortment of bodily apertures.

'Ah!' said Jimmy, experiencing that 'ting' of discovery shared by the marinating Archimedes and the scrumping Newton. 'Tits are not just tits, they're birds! Thrush is birds. And I bet siskins is birds. Stephanie's got a bird table.' Jimmy looked up at the commander with contempt. 'You silly bugger. You've got a real dirty mind.'

'That's what you should do. Build yourself a bird table,' said Stephanie. 'Think what fun it would be if you put it up outside the window of your front room, Jimmy, and watched all the birds coming to it.'

'I couldn't afford to put out scraps,' said Jimmy.

'Don't worry, I would give you some,' said the commander. 'I think your idea's brilliant, Stephanie.'

'It's not that good,' said Kelvin.

'Yes it is,' replied the commander. He was still easing himself back into favour after his embarrassment. 'Stephanie,' he had said, 'let me buy you a drink.'

'I'll have a beer,' Kelvin had said.

'Mine's a whisky,' said Jimmy. 'Perhaps your mind ain't so dirty after all.'

That had helped, but the price had been high: £6.32.

'But I don't know how to build a bird table,' Jimmy whined. 'And I couldn't afford to even if I did.'

'As I said, I could help you,' said the commander. 'Even better, why don't you get our new millionaire to buy one for you.'

'Archie Spontini?' said Jimmy doubtfully.

'I'm supposed to be seeing him tomorrow about my cattle,' said Bill. 'You come round with me and we'll see if he's good for a few quid.'

'Yes,' Stephanie went on, 'your cottage would be a marvellous place for one, Jimmy. With the church opposite and that little wood, you'd attract all sorts of species. You might even get your name in the paper.'

'Me? In the *Gazette*? I ain't had my name in the *Gazette* since 1932 when that horse kicked me and broke my leg. Page 1, that were.'

'It would happen again. Everyone's interested in rare birds. The *Gazette* would report any that you saw. They'd put in your name and probably your photo as well.'

Jimmy mulled it over. 'How would I know if it was a rare bird or not?'

'You'd look it up in a bird book,' said Stephanie patiently.

'Ah! But I can't afford a bird book.'

'I've got an old one I could lend you,' said Stephanie.

'I don't want someone else's cast-offs.'

'I'll give you a new one,' said the commander. He was again on the receiving end of a battery of curious eyes. He had to pay for his *faux pas*, but he had no need to go over the top. 'Oh, I won't actually buy one. The book club computer got in a dither and tried to bury us in books. I've got three bird books and eight copies of a Jeffrey Archer novel, if anybody should want one . . .'

Jimmy thought about it. 'What's to stop me saying I saw an ostrich or something, so that I got into the papers?'

'If you said you saw an ostrich, people probably wouldn't believe you,' explained Stephanie.

'They might if I saw a kite.'

'Well, yes, I suppose they might. But it's a bit premature to talk about what you're going to see before you've even set up a table.'

'I could put out a nice bit of carrion. That'd attract a kite.'

'It might, but it doesn't necessarily work that way. If you put out fish, you would be unlikely to get a penguin.'

'I suppose not.' Jimmy thought some more. 'Yeah! That would do it. I get me little .177 air gun: anything comes, *bang!* I shoot it. Then I wouldn't need a book 'cos I could bring the corpses round and you could tell me if the *Gazette*'d be interested.'

'Jimmy!' gasped Stephanie.

'Sure, and that way if I got me a kite nobody could call me a liar.'

'A kite!' snorted Kelvin. 'Don't be daft, a kite's the size of a pheasant. You'd need a .22 at least.'

'Pheasant!' said Jimmy. 'I'd get the squire's pheasants coming from his wood. I could catch them with gin traps!'

'You can't do that these days!' spluttered Stephanie.

'She's right,' said Bill. 'You know perfectly well that the squire can't afford to put down pheasants any more.'

Stephanie slammed down her glass of Perrier water. 'You put up a bird table, Jimmy,' she said, a quaver in her voice, 'you even *try* to put up a bird table and you'll be in the papers all right. I'll have you in front of the magistrates before you can say "cock robin".'

'But there's got to be some sport in it,' said Jimmy.

'A bird table is for feeding birds,' said Stephanie, adopting the tone of a schoolmistress. 'Feeding birds is not a blood sport.'

'No,' said Kelvin, 'just bloody boring.'

'And not much of a hobby neither,' agreed Jimmy sullenly. 'No, I'd like my photo in the paper but this here bird table definitely ain't the hobby for me.'

'Don't forget, there'll be free money from Archie,' said Bill, reminding him of first principles. 'There might even be a bit left over after you've put up a table.'

Stephanie's glare cut like a laser through the halo of cigarette smoke around Jimmy's head.

'Course, money ain't everything,' said Jimmy. He fidgeted in his seat, fidgeted with his pint, fidgeted with his cigarette.

The pub waited.

'On the other hand,' he said thoughtfully, 'a reasonable man would have to give it a bit of proper consideration.'

Archie was good for £20.

Jimmy reeled out of the pub at closing time the following afternoon having drunk half of it. Turning left, away from the church, he tacked his way down the street.

Since the start of the season was still a month away, there were no tourists about. Jimmy made his way down the hill, past the post office, the café and the general store towards the fifteenth-century stone bridge over the river which had been the catalyst in the creation of Moorcombe.

Just short of the bridge, Jimmy turned right and stopped, swaying slightly. His goal was the second of three cottages. Those flanking it were still simple cob dwellings, one thatched and the other lidded with corrugated iron.

The third was different.

It was thatched, but the thatch was orange plastic. The walls were baby-bum pink, the shutters framing the windows were purple and the front garden had been concreted, save for a small goldfish pond over which a polychromatic gnome dangled a fishing rod. The shubunkin in the pool had been hoovered up by kingfisher and heron, but the gnome still dangled a fishing rod above it, although the grotesque malevolence of its features may have been due to indifferent oriental craftsmanship rather than its own opinion of its fate.

A woman in her mid-forties, wearing a lime-green nylon house-coat with pink fur trimming was working in the garden with a bucket and a mop.

Jimmy leaned gingerly on the white wrought-fibreglass gate which had a dove as its central motif.

'Afternoon, Mandy.'

The woman looked up. Her hair was raven, her eyelids blue

27

and her lashes could have doubled as draught excluders. 'Hullo, Jimmy. Lovely day.'

Jimmy considered. 'Seasonal, I suppose. Could do with a drop of warm rain to get the grass started. What are you doing?'

'Gardening. The bleach in lavatory cleaner brings up the concrete lovely.'

'It does that,' agreed Jimmy.

Jimmy was one of the few wholehearted admirers of the transformation that Mandy and her husband Keith had brought about in their home. Keith had been a butcher in Reading but he was now one of the army who could be described as jobbing builders. His ownership of a cement mixer and a pick-up truck that was only three years old put him amongst the élite.

'I was wondering if you could give me a bit of advice, Mandy.'

'Your wish is my command, Jimmy.' She fluttered her eyelashes at him.

Mandy's self-image was that of a Sindy doll. It would have been more accurate as a feminine version of Margaret Thatcher.

'I've saved £10 so's I can build a bird table and I was wanting something really pretty and tasteful.'

Mandy clapped her hands together. 'Ooh! How exciting! Why don't you come in for a sherry and we'll have a little chatette about it.'

Before the pub opened on Sunday morning, Jimmy asked interested parties round for the unveiling of the bird table. It took place on the small patch of lawn behind his cottage.

In an ideal world, the cottage would have been razed to allow a decent human habitation to take its place. *Sans* electricity, *sans* plumbing, *sans* everything, it had only an immaculate garden with which Jimmy infuriated the commander by out-onioning and out-leeking him every year at the horticultural show.

Nevertheless the visitors gasped with admiration.

They were faced with a plywood replica of the parish church. It lay in the centre of a platform which, Mandy explained, was the graveyard. The scale was quite accurate although the

edifice was pierced by roof-high Gothic doors to allow birds access to the interior. The upper part of the tower formed a nest-
box with the entrance where the clock should have been. The
creation glowed under multitudinous layers of glossy varnish.

Jimmy was delighted. 'It's beautiful, innit? Them birds
don't know how lucky they be, having a real work of art to eat
their dinner in.'

'It is very fine,' agreed Stephanie. 'It looks quite serviceable
too.'

'I made it,' said Keith. He was a ferrety little man, reputed to have a secret life as a Casanova of awesome potency. Malcolm was terrified of him.

'Congratulations.'

'It was my idea, you know,' said Mandy. 'Keith just did as he was told.'

'So I hear. You're very clever,' said Stephanie.

'I know. My Napoleon had a train set when he was a little boy. It had a church which played the first bars of *O Come All Ye Faithful* when the power was on. The budgie got inside and was electrocuted and I thought then that a bigger one would make a lovely bird table.'

'It wasn't electrocuted, dear,' said Keith. 'It strangled itself on the little wires.'

'It was electrocuted,' said Mandy, allowing just a hint of steel into her voice.

'Does this one play a tune?' asked the commander nervously.

'Cor!' said Jimmy. 'That'd be grand! It could play *Widecombe Fair* or one of them Vera Lynn songs.'

'I could fix something up,' said Keith. 'It would cost a bit, though. We'd need a tape loop and a recorder of some kind. It would need to be well protected from the weather.'

'Keith! It's a bird table. You'd frighten them off,' said Stephanie. 'Birds sing, anyway. That'd be better than Vera Lynn. And it would be live.'

'You most certainly will not fix something up,' said Mandy. 'It was not part of my original design.'

'Only because it didn't occur to you, dear,' replied Keith.

'It's because she's an artist,' said Stephanie firmly. 'No true person of taste would play music from a bird table.'

'Precisely,' agreed Mandy.

'Let's put out some food,' suggested Stephanie, changing the subject.

'Yes,' said Jimmy. 'The pub opens in five minutes. Commander, you said you'd bring something.'

'I've been collecting bits and pieces for a few days,' he said. 'Elfrieda helped as well.'

The commander had brought along a wicker shopping bag loaded with little newspaper-wrapped parcels, rather like an order from a Chinese take-away. He placed it on the lawn by the table and laid out his wares.

'That looks like the remains of a chicken curry,' said Mandy, examining the contents of the largest parcel.

'Yes. We had it for supper on Thursday. Green chilli chicken. It was jolly good.'

'I'm not sure that curry is quite the thing for a bird table,' said Stephanie.

'Look at all that gravy,' said Jimmy. 'I'm not putting that out. It'll make a disgusting mess of the varnish.'

The commander looked rather hurt. 'You could drain the gravy off.'

'It's still revolting. It's chicken, so putting it on a bird table is encouraging cannibalism, and you can't go around doing that in a house of God. What else have you got in those?'

'Some apple crumble and a bit of bread.'

'What sort of bread? Proper shop bread?'

'No, Elfrieda baked it. It makes very good toast.'

Jimmy gave a grunt of displeasure. 'The crumble'll be all sticky and your bread'll just turn into mush in the rains. It'll spoil it.'

'It is *meant* to be a bird table,' said Keith mildly.

'It's more than a bird table,' said Mandy, as a vagrant spring trickle of sun leaked through the grey clouds to highlight the gleaming creation. 'Jimmy's right. It's a piece of sculpture. We could cover the graveyard with polythene and put food on that.'

'But the dirty little buggers would go inside and shit in the nave.'

'Line the whole damn thing with plastic, then,' suggested the commander.

'That's a good idea,' said Jimmy, and he did.

For a fortnight Jimmy banged on the window or threw a stone whenever a messy bird dared step upon the hallowed ground of his bird table.

The commander's curry sprouted asbestos-stomached wriggling things which moved inside for sanctuary from the robins and blackbirds who made hit-and-run raids against them whenever Jimmy's attention was elsewhere.

But one of Jimmy's missiles went astray and crashed into the tower, demolishing half the crenellations and dislodging the east wall. Half a hundred maggots were expelled from the choir

into the graveyard where they were snapped up by the blue tits.

Too many ecclesiastical buildings have been spoiled by unsympathetic restoration and, although Jimmy did his best, he was no Gilbert Scott. Nails poked through the north and south walls of the nave and the clerestory, while repeated hammer blows weakened the foundations of the tower, giving it a 10-degree list.

Mandy's concept had lost its lustre, so Jimmy removed the plastic and piled food on top of it. The church was slowly swamped under porridge, tinned steak and mashed potatoes, along with exotic additions from the commander's more affluent table.

But Jimmy was unenthusiastic. 'Little squeaky brown buggers and lots of them tits,' was his standard response to an inquiry about what visited it. After a month the pub lost interest until Jimmy brought the subject up again.

'Commander, I was wondering if you might bring food for my birds a bit more regular. That moosey stuff that you eat for your breakfast is best. That and the boiled pig's head. They picked away at that for days and days. It really lured them in.'

Stephanie was delighted. 'Oh good! I knew you'd find it

fascinating. What was it that got you interested? I've been getting a woodpecker.'

'I don't know about a woodpecker. There's something with a spotty chest. I think it may be a mavis and all them little tit things. But I never thought a bird table would be this exciting.'

'Exciting?'

A doubt began to grow within Stephanie's breast. The commander articulated it for her.

'You haven't gone and got another gun, have you?' he accused.

'No, of course not.'

'Are you quite sure?' questioned Stephanie.

'Sure, I'm sure. What'd I want a gun for? I get all the sport I want without one.'

'Sport? You're up to something, Jimmy. We agreed before you put the thing up that it's not a sport.'

'It is behind my cottage.' Jimmy hugged himself, chuckling evilly.

The pub looked at him with alarm.

'I don't know what you think you're up to, Jimmy,' said Kelvin. 'But it's got to be no good. You'd better watch yourself. The law gets very nasty these days if they catch you killing the wrong kind of bird. You can shoot the dull ones like crows, sparrows and starlings, but the pretty ones have all been conservationized now.'

Jimmy sniffed. 'Anyway, I ain't up to nothing. I'm just enjoying nature.' He took a draught from his pint – it was Thursday evening – and looked craftily round the room. 'Mind you, killing's natural, innit?'

Stephanie was not the only patron to swallow her beer the wrong way. 'Jimmy,' she gasped eventually, 'I'm coming round tomorrow to put a stop to whatever it is you're doing.'

Jimmy chortled contentedly. 'You won't be able to do a damn thing about it, but turn up tomorrow. Round 4 pm, if you want to see some fun.'

The following afternoon, Jimmy was there in carpet slippers to greet his guests. He led them through the clutter of bamboo canes and tools strewn across the tiny hall of the cottage. They ducked their heads under the door frame to enter his front room.

Amid a sea of cardboard boxes and old newspapers he had set a table for afternoon tea by the window in full view of the bird table. Stephanie had not seen it since its accident.

'What on earth has happened to it?' she cried.

'It got a bit broke,' confessed Jimmy.

'And what have you got on it. You're not poisoning them are you?'

'No, that's pigmeal. Frank Mattock had a bag that was piddled on by a cow and he kindly gave it to me for the birds. Sit yourselves down and have a cup of tea.'

'This is a very impressive spread,' said the commander, surveying the table. Jimmy had used his pension to kill a fatted mouse. Pieces of bread spread with meat paste, plates of biscuits and a buttercup-coloured iced cake dotted with violet roses covered the table. 'Does it matter where we sit?'

'No, it's all the same.'

Jimmy bustled through to the kitchen to return bearing a large brown teapot. There was silence for a few moments save for the tinkle of spoons in teacups and the click of Kelvin's false teeth as he chomped his way through a block of bread.

'This is very kind of you, Jimmy. A real treat,' said Stephanie. She looked dubiously at the cake which Jimmy was cutting. Of that variety that come in cardboard boxes, it obviously retained no hint of its original freshness.

She looked through the window. The pyramid of piddled pigmeal, which filled the graveyard and spilled through into the aisles, was covered in a crowd of tits – great, blue, coal and the odd willow. 'It all looks very innocent. What is it that you're up to?'

'I'm up to nothing,' said Jimmy. 'Have a bit of cake.'

'Thank you,' said Kelvin, neatly lifting it off the plate.

Stephanie began to relax. 'I think you were having me on in the pub, Jimmy. There's nothing wrong out there.'

'I told you so,' said Jimmy with a smile. 'But it'll be quite interesting at four o'clock. Have a biscuit.'

'Thank you. You've got something exciting that visits, haven't you?'

Jimmy's smile grew broader. 'Exactly, my dear! Have another cup of tea, Commander.'

'Thank you,' said the commander.

The ritual of tea continued to be played out to Jimmy's satisfaction.

Apart from Kelvin, who moved through the cake with steady concentration, the guests did not find it easy. Jimmy's cigarette was, as always, stuck to his bottom lip covering the food with a Pompeii-like film of ash. Their host did not eat. He just looked on with the quiet satisfaction of one who knows he has done all he can to make his party a success and now leaves it to the guests.

At 3.55 pm Kelvin belched, pushed his plate back and gave tongue. 'Very nice, Jimmy,' he said approvingly. 'I like a nice gateau. What happens now? Do we start shooting the birds?'

Jimmy cackled, rubbing his hands together. 'We now enjoy the sport of kings. Help me shift the table.'

Stephanie smiled. 'You've got a nuthatch, haven't you?'

The four chairs were set in a semi-circle facing the window. Jimmy opened it a few inches and lowered himself into the centre chair. He gestured to the others. 'Come on! Sit down! We don't want to miss anything.'

'I'm really delighted that you're getting so much fun from this,' said Stephanie.

'I am that, my dear. I'm right pleased you said I take up this here hobby.'

They sat, looking through the glass at the tits.

'It's jolly interesting, Jimmy,' said the commander after a minute or two's silence, 'and the glass is very clean. But are we waiting for something, or is this it?'

'We're waiting. It's come just about now for the past few days. Now and about 10 in the morning.'

'It's not a cat, is it?' asked the commander. 'You don't get a cat chasing them all away?'

'You wouldn't let a cat do that, would you?' said Stephanie worriedly.

'Course not. I shoot any bloody cat that scared my little birdies away. Just wait.'

It was only another couple of minutes, but that was long

enough for Kelvin's eyelids to begin to droop. However, the other three saw it all right. They heard it, too.

The table suddenly exploded into activity. Birds hurtled off it in every direction.

Only 18 inches in front of the glass, there was a swoosh of sound and a tiny dry thud as a blue tit was snatched from the air.

Barrel-rolling over the hedge at the end of Jimmy's garden was a sparrowhawk with its prey clutched in its claws.

All that was left to show that the garden had ever held a single bird were three feathers – two yellow and one blue – drifting slowly across the window.

'Good God!' exclaimed the commander.

'What is it?' shouted Kelvin, jerking his eyes open.

Stephanie slowly opened her mouth and shut it again but nothing came out.

Jimmy looked at his guests and emitted a horrible wheezy laugh.

'Ain't nothing in the rule book says you can't put out birds on your bird table to be eaten. Mother Nature's way, innit?'

Chapter Three

Prudence's Secret

PRUDENCE HAD a secret. It was hardly fair: her life appeared to be so utterly predictable that nobody could have suspected it. The commander first brought the matter to the notice of the Hunted Hind.

He mentioned it during a lull in the conversation. Lulls were not infrequent when patrons, slack-jawed, with the electricity spluttering feebly through their brain cells, stared dully at the walls.

'Is Prudence all right, Kelvin?'

Kelvin jumped. So did most of the others. 'What?'

'Sorry. I was just wondering if Prudence was all right. I saw her on the road at the end of your lane this morning picking flowers.'

'Picking flowers? But there aren't any gardens up there.'

'Picking wild flowers. Meadowsweet, actually.'

'Picking weeds! Prudence! This morning! She should have been clearing the ditch down at the bottom of Rushy Meadow. Are you sure it was her?'

'Yes. She looked up and smiled and waved as I passed.'

'It can't have been Prudence,' said Bill decisively. 'She never smiles and waves.'

'It was her. Honestly,' insisted the commander. 'That wasn't all. She was looking rather odd so I slowed down to get a closer look and she was wearing make-up. Quite definitely.'

It was a highly unlikely story, but the commander's insistence forced Kelvin to take it seriously.

'You don't think she can have lost her marbles, do you?' he asked anxiously. 'Her mother's uncle Joseph thought he was a heron when he got on a bit.'

'Really?'

'Yes. He used to stand all day in the river trying to catch fish. Poor old bugger was put away after he nearly drowned. Tried to catch them in his teeth, you see.'

Bill grunted. 'She may be mazed, but if it's because of Joseph Tout, half the bloody village'd be round the twist. His blood's in me and thee, Kelvin, as well as Prudence.'

'She's in love,' said Annie.

The pub considered this possibility.

The commander spread his lips in a grimace. 'It's the obvious conclusion. Anyone else and there wouldn't have been any need to think further, but one sort of discounts it as far as Prudence is concerned.'

'Has she been seen anywhere near Willie Bladderwick's barn?' asked Annie. 'That's a sure sign.'

'Not Prudence, not her, not ever,' insisted Kelvin.

Lindy sniffed. 'I think your attitude is most unfair. Prudence is a normal woman and subject to all the normal desires.'

'You couldn't call Prudence normal, not really,' he replied. 'Don't get me wrong: she's a good worker and doesn't complain and she doesn't spent money, but she's never been like other girls. Her mother sent her into town to buy some nylons once and she came back with a lamb castrator instead. That's not really normal now, is it?'

'Some people are late developers.'

'It's true,' agreed Ivor. 'She's been showing the signs. Look at her sweaters. They've got very tight in the last few months.'

Kelvin sighed. 'It would be nice to think that Prudence was normal, but she never sees anyone. The last time she was off the farm was a fortnight ago Sunday when she came here.'

'It might be a rep she's taken a shine to,' suggested Ivor.

'Reps only call on us once,' said Kelvin. 'They know better than to come back a second time.'

'She could be up to anything in the evening,' said Bill. 'You'd never know about it, Kelvin, 'cos you're always here.'

'In the evening she milks and feeds the calves and moves the fences and things like that. She doesn't knock off till dark and then she goes to bed because she's up at 5 every morning.'

Bill grunted in envy. 'There's no doubt about it. You've got a real treasure there.'

'I don't pay her either,' boasted Kelvin. 'I used to give her a couple of quid a week ten years ago, but then I stopped and she's never asked for anything since. She's a good daughter is my Prudence.'

'Poor creature!' exclaimed Lindy. 'Still, it's got to be either love or she's flipped under the strain of having you as a father. You don't get women of forty going around picking meadow-sweet for no reason at all.'

'That's quite true,' agreed Kelvin. 'D'ya think there's any chance of you coming out to take a look at her, Lindy? Or would it be better if I took her to the doctor?'

'I'd mind your own business, Kelvin,' replied Lindy tartly. 'If her only symptom of illness is putting on a bit of lipstick and picking wild flowers, the world would be a better place if everyone had it.'

'Kelvin would look nice in a bit of lipstick,' said Jimmy.

Kelvin frowned. 'It's not something to joke about. I really would be grateful if you'd come out, just to see her. I'll give you a bag of potatoes.'

'And a dozen eggs?'

Kelvin considered. 'Okay.'

'Right, then. I'll pop in tomorrow morning before I start my rounds. Say half-eight?'

'I suppose you'd better come in and have a cup of tea.'

The next morning Kelvin, dressed but shoeless, greeted Lindy in the doorway, peering anxiously over her shoulder towards his farm buildings.

'She'll be in for her breakfast in a minute,' he said. 'She's just finishing off the milking.'

'I'll wait to share Prudence's breakfast,' replied Lindy rather acidly. 'I had to skip mine in order to be here.'

'There'll be only porridge,' said Kelvin.

'Porridge!' exclaimed Lindy, wrinkling her nose. 'What about the groaning farmhouse table with thick rashers of bacon and eggs and things?'

'We did send a pig to the abattoir the other day and it was going to be bacon, but the meat was condemned. Didn't think there'd be much wrong with it, myself. Just a few abcesses and boils which could have easily been cut out, but Prudence went and left it there. So we're out of bacon. The chickens are all going broody and laying in the hedges too.'

'All right,' said Lindy. 'I'll make do with porridge.'

'Prudence'll be here in a minute and she'll put it on,' said Kelvin. He led the way through to the kitchen, a long dank passage that lay behind the sitting room.

Lifting a pile of yellowing copies of the *Sun* from a chair, he dusted it down with a greasy cloth from the sink.

'Sit down here, Lindy, next to the Aga – the warmest seat in the house. I'll put on a kettle.'

Kelvin moved the heavy cast-iron kettle across to the hob and it began to simmer almost immediately. Swilling a couple of mugs beneath the tap, he dropped in tea-bags. He picked up a grey plastic jug from the table and gave it a sniff.

'The milk's a little bit off. Would you rather wait until Prudence brings some?'

'I'll have it black please,' replied Lindy.

Kelvin poured the water into the mugs and the bags floated to the top like drowned mice. He pulled out another chair and sat down opposite, taking a slurping gulp of his tea.

He grinned at her.

'There's no point in grinning at me like a great pudding. There's nothing I can do for Prudence. I only came out of friendship and because I need some potatoes. Where are they?'

'I'll get them when you go.'

'You'll do no such thing. You'll get them now.'

'I can't. They're out in the barn. I'll send Prudence to get them after she's had her breakfast.'

'Kelvin, do you leave that girl to do everything for you?'

'No, of course not. But I give her shelter and food in my own house and don't charge her a penny for it. It's only right she helps with odd jobs when I'm too busy.'

'Kelvin. Go and get me my potatoes. Now!'

'I've got my slippers on.'

'Go and put your boots on. If you've got any.'

'Oh, all right.' Kelvin pottered off, muttering to himself.

Casting her eye round the kitchen, Lindy found a fork with which she removed the tea-bag from her mug. She looked at the fork, held it up to the light and clicked her tongue in irritation. She crossed to the earthenware sink and washed it. She then washed the sink, its surround and the table. After wiping the top of the stove and re-washing a pan, she found a box of oats, added salt and water and began to make the porridge.

Prudence quietly slipped through the door and into the kitchen. Kelvin, carrying a bag of potatoes, was in pursuit.

'You should have had some potatoes already bagged up. I've had to go out and get them myself. I told you last night that Lindy was coming round this morning.'

'You didn't, Dad.'

'Yes I did. 'Course I did. I shouted up the stairs to you after I came back from the pub. I shouted loudly too. I'd've woken you up if you'd been asleep. So you can't pretend you didn't know about it.'

'What time did you get in?'

'Oh, not late. Ten-thirty-odd.'

'I didn't get back till midnight,' said Prudence.

'What?' The sack fell from nerveless fingers. 'Out till midnight? What's wrong with you? You know your mother always insisted you were in bed by half-past eight!'

'That's when I had to walk to school the next morning, Dad. I left school twenty-five years ago.'

'Even so! Twelve o'clock! I'm very disappointed in you! You knew quite well that you were milking this morning! You can't expect me to do it for you.'

42

Prudence gave a wry smile. 'I didn't, Dad. I've just done the milking.'

'That's not the point! And what are you doing wearing rubber gloves?'

'Hullo, Lindy.'

'Morning, Prudence. Does he go on at you like this the whole time?' Lindy indicated Kelvin with a curt nod.

Prudence smiled once more. 'Oh you mustn't mind Dad. He does go on a bit.' She peeled off her gloves to reveal that her hands were covered in white ointment.

Kelvin recoiled from the sight in horror. 'What's wrong with your hands, child? You haven't been doing the milking with some foul disease? You ought to know better than to show them to Lindy. She's the district nurse and might not like you polluting the milk.'

'It's just udder cream, Dad.'

'Udder cream? Why do you want to go putting udder cream all over yourself?'

'I saw an advert for soft hands on the telly the other day and the stuff they used looked just like udder cream.'

'You don't want to go and get soft hands, you silly girl! It's taken years to get hands like yours.' He turned to Lindy, holding up his own horny protuberances. 'I could shift concrete blocks all day with these hands and never feel it. They're a farmer's most valuable tools, his hands.'

'Prudence might want hands that don't ladder every pair of stockings she puts on,' said Lindy.

'But she doesn't need to wear stockings, Lindy! Have you ever heard of a farm worker in stockings? Prudence wears woolly socks in her gumboots.'

'But if she goes out of an evening, she might want to wear a skirt.'

'Yes, missy!' exclaimed Kelvin, turning to Prudence who was rinsing her hands under the tap. 'What *were* you doing out until late last night? Was it anything to do with them weeds the commander saw you picking? You've got a fancy man, haven't you? Who is it?'

'None of your business, Dad.'

'That's the stuff!' said Lindy.

'It is my business! You're my daughter! Tell her, Lindy.'

'He's your father, Prudence, and you have my deepest sympathy.'

'That's not what I mean. She has a duty to me! I might have needed her or something.'

'Something?' asked Lindy.

'Yes.' Kelvin pulled out a chair and sat down at the table. 'I . . . I could have been worried about her. She might have been dead in a ditch. It's normal that a father should be concerned about what his daughter gets up to.'

'I was out, Dad.'

'I know. But where?'

'Don't you damn well tell him, Prudence. It's nothing to do with him!'

'Here!' exclaimed Kelvin. 'Whose side are you on?'

'Prudence's,' replied Lindy crisply.

'I don't really mind if you know, Dad,' said Prudence, drying her hands on a towel hanging over the rail in front of the stove. 'I've been seeing Archie.'

'Archie? Archie Spontini? What on earth do you want to see him for?'

Lindy sighed. 'You are so thick, Kelvin.'

'What do you mean?' Kelvin lowered his brows aggressively. He snorted. 'Huh! You're not trying to say that they've been up to anything!'

'Why shouldn't we be?' asked Prudence.

44

'Good grief, girl! You can't be carrying on with him! Archie Spontini! He's a cross between Joy and a bloody foreigner! He's got money, I grant you, but what would your mother say?'

'Not a lot,' replied Prudence. 'Not after more than twenty years in her grave.'

Kelvin was not listening. He shook his head. 'The shame of it! The Morchards were always a cut above the Chilcotts anyway, but after Joy married that there Eyetie . . . and there's bad blood in that fellow. Look how his father behaved.' He shook his head decisively. 'I forbid you to go out with him! The matter is closed. Is the porridge ready yet, Lindy?'

Lindy took a ladleful of porridge from the pot and poured it on the pine table in front of Kelvin. She poured it from a height so that it splashed over him.

'Get your own porridge, you miserable old sod!'

Prudence stepped smartly aside to allow room for her father to leap to his feet and dance round the room, holding his trousers away from his legs. 'Aahh! It's hot. Didn't you see there wasn't a bowl? Ow! Ooh!'

Prudence finished drying her hands and pulled three bowls out of a cupboard. 'Don't make such a fuss, Dad, and I'll see Archie as often as I like.'

Kelvin stopped dancing. 'What? Aren't you feeling well? Didn't you hear what I said? You've never gone against me before.'

'Never wanted to do anything like this before so I didn't need to.'

'Well done!' cried Lindy. 'You tell him.'

'I will if I want to,' replied Prudence. 'Sit down, Lindy. You are having breakfast with us?'

'Er . . . yes.' Lindy sat down.

'And you sit down too, Dad.' Kelvin sat. 'Now listen. I'm an adult and I can have a relationship with whom I like when I like and it's nobody's affair but his and mine.'

'That's obvious enough,' said Lindy. She received a cold glance from Prudence and hastily continued, 'I mean, if you're having an affair, it's obvious that it's yours and not anyone else's.'

Kelvin stirred. 'You're not having it off with him, are you?'

'Making love is nice.'

45

Kelvin gasped. 'Shameless!'

'You see Chastity Trotter, you old goat!' said Prudence.

'That's different. I'm a man and I'm married. How did you know, anyway?'

'I found her corset in your bed when I was changing the sheets fifteen years ago.'

'I think perhaps I'd better skip breakfast and get on with my rounds,' said Lindy tactfully. 'I'm not sure that I ought to be part of this conversation. Anyway, you're obviously not ill, Prudence.'

'Ill? Whoever suggested I was ill? But there is one thing, though. I know all the symptoms in cattle and sheep, but is there any easy way to tell when a human being gets pregnant?'

Over the next few days, the Hunted Hind noticed that Kelvin was on edge. It was most solicitous. Hoping to discover the cause, Mandy even went so far as to buy him a drink.

But it was Bill who found out. He told them about it on Friday evening.

'I saw Prudence at market this morning and I took her to lunch.'

'You took her to lunch?' Jimmy sounded surprised. Although Bill was extravagant compared with Kelvin, he knew the value of a penny and usually invested his lunches in shady dealers with whom he might do business.

'She told me what was upsetting Kelvin.'

'Ah!' exclaimed Jimmy. 'And it was worth a lunch?'

'Yes. You know what Prudence is like. I asked her what was wrong with him and she said she didn't know. So I said there must be something and she thought for a bit and said that she couldn't think of anything really but it might be because she thought she was pregnant.'

'Pregnant? Prudence?' Jimmy gave a low whistle.

'*Thought* she was pregnant,' emphasized Bill.

'Even so, Prudence!'

In stunned silence the pub digested the fact that Prudence must have or have had a lover. It required a readjustment of its concept of the nature of reality.

'Well, well, well,' said Ivor after a suitable pause. 'Who'd've thought it?'

46

'Typical Prudence,' said the commander. 'Only Prudence would tell people she might be pregnant. Er . . . did she say what made her think so?'

'When she found herself spreading marmalade on a page of *Farming News* and eating it before she went milking,' said Bill.

'It must be hell to be a woman,' said Jimmy with a shudder. 'I'd come back with a load of rabbits after ferreting and my missus, God rest her soul, used to bite off the claws and eat them when she was carrying.'

'Did she say who?' asked the commander.

'Aye, it was a baby. Our Gilbert who's now in Calgary.'

'I'm not talking about your missus, Jimmy. I'm talking about Prudence. Bill, did she say who it was?'

Bill looked mystified. 'Who what was?'

'Don't be dim. Who was the other party involved? You don't get pregnant by yourself.'

Bill groaned and smote his brow. 'I knew there was something!'

Mandy sniffed. 'If it is true, I think it's shocking. She's not married, you know.'

'Nor were you, dear, when you were pregnant with Napoleon,' said Keith.

'Keith! That's simply not true!' Mandy shot him her best ball-squeezing frown.

Keith gulped. 'Anyway, it was a long time ago and you weren't very pregnant.'

'We don't know that Prudence is pregnant yet,' Bill pointed out. 'She only thinks she might be. Lindy told her she'd have to have a test.'

'That's not the point,' said Mandy. 'Even if she wasn't pregnant, the very fact that she thinks she is means that she was up to something that she shouldn't be without a wedding ring on her finger.'

'Don't be ridiculous!' snorted Ivor. 'These days that attitude is out of date everywhere. And it never has been in date round here. Nobody ever even got engaged in the old days until the girl was safely pregnant.'

'But who on earth could Prudence's lover be?' asked the commander.

'It ain't me,' said Jimmy.

I'm going to be a mummy

The latch clicked and the pub door creaked open.

The commander turned. 'Ah! Lindy! Do you know anything about this business with Prudence?'

Lindy's step faltered as she received the full battery of the pub's eyes. 'I don't know what you're talking about.'

'Oh come on! You must do.'

'I don't talk about my patients.'

The door opened once more to admit Prudence and her father.

'No!' Kelvin was saying. 'We will not go in there!'

'But I saw Lindy. Ah! Lindy!'

'Hullo, Prudence,' responded Lindy warily.

'I got my results! I'm all right!'

'Thank heaven for that!'

'Yes, isn't it wonderful!' Prudence beamed round at the assembled patrons.

'All I can say is you're lucky,' said Mandy.

'I know,' said Prudence. 'Imagine it! I'm going to be a mummy!'

Pregnancy had already performed the heroic feat of making Prudence almost beautiful. Once it had recovered from the shock, the pub found it impossible not to respond to her transparent delight.

'Congratulations,' said Mandy grudgingly. 'Who's the lucky man?'

'No!' shouted Kelvin, but he was too late.

'Archie Spontini.'

A sigh, like a cat's-paw of wind through a field of ripened oats, rustled round the bar.

'But I'm not going to get married. We have a warm and loving relationship, but marriage is not part of our plans.'

'Jesus!' said Bill. 'He's sold you that one, has he?'

'It's the modern way, you know,' said Prudence.

The pub was temporarily speechless.

Jimmy brought up another engrossing aspect of the revelation. 'What do you think about all this, Kelvin?'

'It's nothing to do with him,' snapped Lindy.

'I didn't say that it was,' replied Jimmy. 'But every man's entitled to an opinion and I'd like to know Kelvin's.'

'I'd rather not give it,' replied Kelvin. 'But I'll tell you one thing. If that Archie bloody Spontini was not in London for a few days, I'd get out my father's old horse whip and thrash him within an inch of his misbegotten life! Taking advantage of a young girl like Prudence! It's shocking!'

'Come on, Dad. He didn't take advantage of me. I knew very well what I was doing.'

'No you didn't! You're an innocent maid.'

'I haven't been innocent since Uncle Charlie cornered me in the tractor shed when I was fourteen.'

'That was different. Charlie were family and he said he was sorry. He was drunk anyway.'

'Being family has nothing to do with it. Archie came over to see you about something but you were at the pub so I took him upstairs.' A grin stole across her face. 'I said I wanted to show him grandfather's ploughing trophies.'

Jimmy shook his head. 'A man has got no chance when faced with a determined woman.'

'You can't say he'd've done that unless he fancied a bit of hanky panky,' said Kelvin.

'We both thought it was very nice and we've been meeting regularly ever since. He's got lovely eyes.'

'Lovely eyes!' said Kelvin, spilling his beer as he rounded on her savagely. 'It's all very well for you, missy, but who's going to do the milking when you go into hospital? And there's the scandal, of course, isn't there? The Morchards have always been among the most respectable families in the area. That's right, isn't it?' He looked round the pub for agreement.

'It's true,' confirmed Bill grudgingly. 'The Morchards have always been well regarded.'

'See, missy? It's a right scandal! Your great-great-grandfather was a Methody lay preacher! I'll bet he's spinning in his grave like the propeller on a jumbo jet at the shame you're bringing on the family!'

The commander cleared his throat uneasily. 'When you think about it, there isn't a scandal unless people are scandalized.'

'Of course people will be scandalized! Having a baby without a husband! It's shocking!'

'But who's being shocked?' asked the commander. 'I'm not. Are you, Ivor?'

'Er . . . no.'

'I'm quite sure Lindy isn't. Annie isn't. Mandy's pretending to be but isn't either and Jimmy's at an age when his only interest is survival until next opening time. So, you see, there's no scandal at all.'

'You're shocked, aren't you, Bill?' demanded Kelvin.

Bill considered. 'No. I'm afraid I can't say I am. In fact I think the idea of Prudence having a baby is rather nice. Prudence is a woman and that's what women are for and it was beginning to look as if she wasn't going to make it.'

'That's perfectly true,' agreed Jimmy.

'There's another thing,' continued Bill. 'You'll have a grandchild, Kelvin. Think on that. The Morchard line will continue.'

'But the little bugger won't be a Morchard!' cried Kelvin. 'He'll be a Spontini! A grandchild of mine with a daft foreign name like that!'

'He'll be a Morchard, Dad,' said Prudence. 'I know how much it means to you. If Brett's born illegitimate, then he'll take my name, you see. He'll be Brett Morchard. I thought his second name might be Kelvin.'

Kelvin frowned. 'That can't be true, can it?'

'She's right,' confirmed Lindy. 'The child will be born a Morchard.'

Kelvin pondered while the pub held its breath. 'It still won't make any difference to him being an Eyetalian, of course.'

'Don't be daft,' scoffed Jimmy. 'A quarter of him will be you, a quarter of him will be your missus (God rest her soul), a quarter will be Joy (God rest hers too) and only the last little bit will be foreign.'

'Won't any of him be me?' asked Prudence.

'Of course it will. You're going to be his mother and half of him will be you.'

Kelvin grunted. 'That'll still leave a quarter of him foreign.'

'Think of the hybrid vigour, Kelvin,' urged Ivor. 'Look at Churchill. His mother was foreign.'

'Yes, but she can't have been Eyetalian. Although, when you think about it, even Her Majesty is half-Scotch and John Shapland's missus over at the four-way cross came from right the other side of the moor.'

'That's right,' confirmed Bill, 'and their boy is chairman of the Young Farmers this year.'

'You see?' said the commander. 'A bit of fresh blood can do wonders!'

'Hmm.' Kelvin sounded unconvinced.

'It'll be great, Dad,' urged Prudence. 'You'll be able to bounce your own grandson on your lap. I bet he'll look just like you.'

'You'll be getting maintenance from Archie, of course, won't you, Prudence?' asked Ivor.

Kelvin's nostrils flared and his ears pricked like a hound's when a fox farts on a day when the scent is good. 'Maintenance? What do you mean?'

'Well, if Archie's willing to acknowledge his paternity, it'll be his responsibility to contribute towards the rearing of the child.'

'Cor! You mean he's going to have to pay us money?'

'Pay Prudence, Kelvin, to help maintain the child.'

'How much will we be able to get, d'ya think?'

'I don't know.'

'Lindy. You must come across lots of bastards. How much are they worth?'

Lindy gritted her teeth but she knew her man well enough not to waste her time in protest. 'About £15 or £20 a week, I'd guess. But that's not all. There'll be child benefit and single parent allowance too.'

'And you should be able to claim him as a dependent against tax,' added Ivor.

Kelvin whistled. 'How long does all that go on for?'

'As long as the child needs it, I suppose. Until it's eighteen.'

'Cor!' exclaimed Kelvin again, rubbing his hands together. 'It's better than the old cattle subsidy!'

'There's another point too,' said Ivor. 'I'm pretty sure that the child will have legal rights on its father's estate.'

'What do you mean?' Kelvin was so intent upon the conversation that he had not even ordered himself a drink.

'So long as Archie has no other heirs, it means the child could well inherit his farm.'

'Jesus! Do you mean that the little bastard would end up with Middlecott? That would make the Morchards the biggest land owners in the parish now that the squire's sold off most of his land.' Kelvin's eyes glowed with a glorious vision of the future. 'Cor! That would be something. I can remember my old granfer saying that his granfer had dreamed about getting Middlecott after the war. We did very well with potatoes in the war. But he never managed it. And I might!'

'Which war?' asked Bill with interest. 'I don't ever remember potatoes on Southcott.'

'I don't rightly know its name. It was the one when one of the Bladderwicks went to Exeter to sell some horses and was press-ganged into the navy.'

'Archie might sell the farm before he dies,' pointed out Ivor mildly.

'Never!' scorned Kelvin. 'His name may be Spontini, but he's a Chilcott and Chilcotts don't sell land.'

'I bought my place off Joe Chilcott in the fifties,' said Ivor.

'Yes, but he wasn't one of the proper Chilcotts. He came from up country somewhere – near Bath, I think – and only got the farm because he was a cousin of Willy Nurcombe who shot himself in the Depression.'

Jimmy nodded his head sagely. 'They were poor stock, the Nurcombes. Mary Nurcombe could never make decent brawn.'

'I hate to strike a discordant note, Kelvin,' said the commander, 'but Archie doesn't even know that Prudence is pregnant. It seems a little premature to start counting chickens at this stage.'

'I don't see why. If he's the father, that's all there is to it.'

'Yes, but it's one thing to admit to having an ... er ... *tendresse* with someone and it's quite another to have a child.'

'Why? It's perfectly natural to have children after a bit of hanky panky. If it weren't like that, there wouldn't be anyone in the world.'

'Yes, but these days there's contraception and abortion. The average chap doesn't expect to have to fork out ... er ... £20,000 over a couple of decades if he indulges in a bit of hanky panky.'

'Well he bloody well ought to.' Kelvin rubbed his hands in glee. '£20,000!'

'Would you pay if Chastity Trotter got pregnant?' asked Prudence.

'Here!' exclaimed Kelvin indignantly. 'What I get up to with Chastity is none of your damn business! Anyway, it would be a bloody miracle at her age. She's well past that sort of thing and even if she weren't, it would as likely be a dozen other people as me. Her Charles and Anne used to get birthday presents from half the men in the parish. Including you, Jimmy.'

'That's just 'cos I felt sorry for them, being fatherless.'

'If Archie's got any sense, he'll make the farm over to the boy so that he can avoid death duties. Then I could look after it for him. I could sell off the house and do pedigree Herefords on the water meadows both sides and perhaps even a few acres of swedes. Think on it, Prudence!'

'I don't want Brett to be a farmer. I want him to be a television presenter,' said Prudence. 'He should have a nice clean job with a regular pension at the end of it.'

'Don't be silly,' replied Kelvin, a puzzled look on his face. 'He'll be a Morchard. Of course he'll be a farmer. I think we all ought to have a drink on Archie to celebrate the fact that he's going to be a father.'

'I still think it's a bit premature,' warned the commander.

'Nonsense! I'll go and tell him when he gets back and have a chat with him about the maintenance money and give him some advice about passing the farm over to me. The sooner he starts paying, the better. After all, Prudence has got to take care of herself when she's carrying and won't be able to do some of the heavy work like shifting fertilizer around and I'll have to hire someone to do it. He's going to have to pay. Randy bugger!' Kelvin rubbed his hands together, producing a sound like mating tortoises. 'Let's have the drinks, then! Mine's a large whisky!'

Chapter Four

Ferox

'I WENT for a walk up the river this morning,' said Ivor, toying with a whisky and soda.

The pub had been sitting wondering what might be offered for its entertainment. Once the church-goers had discussed the sermon, the session at lunchtime on Sunday often petered out into silence for minutes at a time.

'What did you do that for?' asked Kelvin. He was a farmer and farmers do not go for walks in the countryside, any more than miners go potholing.

'It was such a lovely morning. I saw a swallow. First one of the season.'

'Swallows have been around for weeks,' stated Kelvin.

'I think there's a ferox in Ash Pool,' said Ivor.

'What on earth is a ferox?' asked Stephanie.

'You a so-called nature expert and you don't know?' sneered Kelvin.

'No, I don't,' replied Stephanie. 'You tell me.'

'A ferox? Well, it's obvious isn't it? It's . . . er . . .'

'A cross between a ferret and a fox?' suggested Jimmy. He was joking, making it obvious by poking his tongue into his cheek, but Kelvin was looking at Stephanie and seized on the suggestion.

' 'Course it is. A cross between a fox and a ferret. Like a mule. That's what a ferox is.'

'Don't be silly!' exclaimed Stephanie. 'Foxes and ferrets are not even the same family.'

'Well, of course they're not. I know that. If they had been the same family, it would be incest or something.' Even Kelvin was uneasily aware that his own determination to know everything had left him defending ill-chosen ground.

The pub did not have great confidence in Stephanie. It feared she lacked the killer instinct. She was a teacher. She read the *Guardian* and jogged, and Kelvin had said that he had seen her through her living-room window doing aerobics in a body stocking. On top of that she had blue eyes and brown ringlets, and her normal expression was one of interested benevolence.

However, Little Nell herself would have stuck a shiv into Kelvin's back if the opportunity had presented itself.

Stephanie, sitting with Malcolm at a table a few yards from the bar, smiled up at Kelvin on his stool alongside Bill and Ivor. 'Kelvin. You are not seriously maintaining that ferrets and foxes can successfully mate, are you?'

Kelvin rolled his eyes and waggled his teeth as his mind raced in search of an escape from having to admit error. 'There are some not a million miles from here who have done it with sheep.'

'Foxes?'

'No, people.'

'That's a lie!' exclaimed Jimmy. 'I never!'

'Well, well, well,' said Kelvin. 'I didn't say you did.'

'Well, I never, anyway,' said Jimmy sulkily. He stretched out a claw-like hand to grab a handful of peanuts from the bowl on the bar. At lunchtime on Sunday, nuts were free and sometimes there were even sausage rolls or cheese biscuits.

'This is becoming a bit rich,' said Ivor. 'I think I'd better explain that a ferox is a trout.'

Kelvin continued to distance himself from his explanation. 'It's a bloody silly name for a trout and the river's full of them. There'll be dozens in Ash Pool.'

'It's a special sort of trout. They have them in lochs in Scotland. They're huge and live down at the bottom. I went after them once on a poor day on Loch Awe when nothing else was happening. Put on a minnow and hooked a 10-pounder, and they can be bigger than that. Horrible black thing it was, with a great undershot jaw.'

'They're cannibals, I suppose?' asked Kelvin.

'Yes.'

Kelvin shook his head doubtfully. 'I've heard of cannibal

trout in the river up to 3 or 4 lb. But you won't find anything like that.'

'How do you know there's one of those . . . er . . . feroxes there?' asked Bill. 'Did you actually see it?'

'What I saw was a duckling disappear under the water. It was like that film about the shark. One minute it was there and the next it wasn't.'

Bill frowned. 'Is that all?'

'It's enough, isn't it?'

'Well, no. There could be dozens of explanations for a disappearing duck. It could have just sunk.'

'No it couldn't. Ducks don't sink. They have to work like hell to stay beneath the surface. When they dive, they bob up again like . . . like . . .'

'Corks?' suggested Stephanie.

'Yes! That's what they bob up like. Corks!'

'Okay. It dived then. Ducks do.'

'And never came up? I watched for ten minutes.'

'It was got by a pike or a mink or an otter or a drake.'

'There aren't any pike in the river and anything else must have been wearing aqualungs because it stayed down. It looked just like an ordinary trout rise except that it wasn't a fly but a duckling.'

Stephanie shivered. 'It's a bit creepy. We went swimming in that pool and it's not very nice to think there's something in there like that.'

Kelvin looked at her speculatively. 'Who's "we"?'

'It was in the summer. We had some friends down from Oxford and we all went for a midnight swim. Skinny dipping. It was lovely.'

'It must have been,' said Kelvin wistfully. 'Skinny dipping. It sounds rather fun. I'd like to come along next time.'

'I bet you would,' said Bill. 'You dirty old bugger.'

'Oh, come now,' said Stephanie, 'the naked human body isn't dirty. It's beautiful.'

'Kelvin's isn't.'

'Well, perhaps not. But anyway, I'm not too sure that I'd risk Ash Pool now.'

'You'd be all right, Stephanie,' said Ivor. 'It might be different with Malcolm, though. It's possible that he might have lost the odd portion of his anatomy. A nice fleshy little something dangling down from the surface might well tempt a ferox to take a snap.'

If Stephanie had shivered, Malcolm shuddered. He took a hurried sip of his whisky. 'That's an appalling thought. You won't catch me in there again.'

Kelvin nodded sagely. 'Very wise. It's not something you'd want to risk. I remember when Billy Clattermole's father lost his in a threshing machine. Took away the front of his trousers too. It was a sad business. If Billy Clattermole had been born a year later, he wouldn't have been born at all. That would have been no great loss, mind you.'

'The council ought to do something about it,' said Mandy. 'It's downright dangerous having something like that in the river. What with children playing there and things, it won't be long before someone gets hurt.'

'That's true,' agreed Jimmy. 'A sheep or a cow going down to drink might get dragged under.'

'I think we may be over-reacting,' said Ivor. 'Cases of cattle being attacked by trout are not that common.'

'That's all very well for you to say,' said Kelvin. 'but none of your land goes down to the river. I think we ought to go and get rid of the thing.'

'Yes,' agreed Malcolm eagerly. 'We could go out this afternoon and see if we can catch it. We could have it stuffed and put above the bar.'

Bill was the lone Cassandra. 'All Ivor saw was a sinking duck. The damn thing probably shipped water because it forgot to keep its arse shut.'

'It doesn't really matter,' said Stephanie. 'It'll get everybody away from their TVs on a Sunday afternoon and that's to the good.'

'It'll end in tears, mark my words,' said Bill.

The path towards Ash Pool started on the far side of the bridge at the bottom of the village. Marked by painted red arrows on trees and posts to reassure tourists that they did not enter uncharted wilderness as soon as they were out of sight of their cars, it meandered through a wood carpeted with sorrel, anemones, clumps of primroses and a few harbingers of the mass of bluebells that would last until the canopy shut out the sunlight. It was a fine spring afternoon and the air was pungent with the scent of wild garlic as the sun released the oil from the leaves.

'Bloody stinks, that stuff,' remarked Kelvin, who was carrying a bundle of nylon net. 'I don't know why the squire never cleared this wood. There's a few quid in some of these trees and he'd have got a good grant for planting conifers. It would have cleared out all these weeds.'

'If he'd had any sense, he would have drained it when the grants were high and turned the whole thing into decent pasture,' said Bill. 'Still, it's his own look-out. If he'd had more sense, he wouldn't be down to 400 acres.'

Malcolm sighed but said nothing. He had learned that the gulf between the older natives and born-again conservationists like himself and Stephanie was unbridgeable.

On their right, the river made white water as it hurled itself at the boulders which littered its bed. A thunderstorm had rumbled across the moor the previous night and the flow had still not returned to its normal level.

The river spread itself into Ash Pool where the path descended to water level. Kelvin dumped the nets on a rock as the others filtered down. Jimmy, whose years melted off him when he so choose, puffed down last.

'How deep is it?' asked the commander, looking out over the water.

'Bottomless,' replied Jimmy.

'Bottomless? What do you mean? If you fell in, you wouldn't end up in Australia.'

'You might do. Nobody has ever found the bottom, anyway. A horse bolted with a gypsy caravan and went in and never a trace was ever seen again.'

Malcolm looked at the pool and wrinkled his brow. 'But the horse would have swum and the caravan would have floated.'

'Disappeared. Swallowed up, they were, in its abyss.'

'And how could a horse and caravan get here in the first place?' Malcolm demanded. 'They couldn't have come along this path and there isn't any other way in.'

'There's the old packhorse bridge half a mile upstream,' said Ivor.

'But the very fact that it's a packhorse bridge means that there weren't any wheeled vehicles,' argued Malcolm. 'Anyway, when was this tragedy supposed to have taken place, Jimmy?'

'Dunno. Backalong, I suppose.'

The day had been improving ever since the cock had delivered its shrill clarion into the dying dribble of the thunderstorm. Orange tip butterflies and brimstones lurched spasmodically through the trees and chiff-chaffs chiff-chaffed with the dogged endurance of a cracked record.

'Who's brought their wellies?' asked Kelvin.

'Me,' said Jason Loosemire. As a randy nineteen-year-old, he should have been roaring round the countryside on his motorcycle with a local maiden pressed against his leather-clad back, but the call of the ferox had been stronger. Jason was one of the more respectable of the Loosemire farrow and even held down a job of sorts as builder's labourer, working for Keith.

'Well, get in the river and stretch the nets across the bottom of the pool.'

'But it'll go over my boots.'

'No, it won't. Not if you watch where you put your feet.'

Jason looked at the water without conviction. 'Why does it have to be me?'

'Because you've got wellies. Get on with it, for heaven's sake! We don't want to be here all day.'

Grumbling, Jason gathered a net and stepped into the water. He anchored one end of the net to a tree root and trailed the rest through the shallows behind him. He made the other side, 15 yards away, and sat on a boulder to empty the water out of his boots.

'What do you want me to do now, Kelvin?' he called.

'Stay there!'

'Piss off! I'm coming back over.'

Kelvin tutted in exasperation. 'In that case, make sure that you fix the net properly. If the fish gets through, I'll string your guts round your neck.'

As Jason splashed back, Kelvin undid the straps on his pack and pulled out a gallon plastic container. 'You'd think more of them would have had enough sense to wear wellies,' he grumbled to Bill.

'You aren't,' Stephanie pointed out.

'Of course we're not. We've got more sense, but they haven't got enough. I was buggered if I was going to get wet.' He shook the plastic bottle experimentally.

'What's that?' asked Stephanie.

'In the bottle? That's silage additive, formic acid.'

'What do you do with it?'

'You pour it into the top of the pool and it takes the oxygen out of the water. It's marvellous stuff. It kills all the fish and the nets catch them as they drift down.'

There was a few seconds' pause.

'Ivor!' wailed Stephanie. 'Come here a minute!'

Ivor had been engaged in conversation with the commander on the merits of this section of the river valley as a pheasant drive. He looked round at Stephanie's call and walked across the rocks at the river's edge towards her. 'If some of those trees – just a 20-yard strip – were cleared, you'd get some super high birds going across.'

'Oh shut up!' said Stephanie. 'Do you know what Kelvin intends to do?'

'You shouldn't be talking to Ivor like that,' said Jimmy. 'People have to show respect for each other, Stephanie. You don't go around telling people to shut up.'

'Oh, I don't know,' said Kelvin, pulling a couple of evil-looking collapsible gaffs from his bag and erecting them with a practised flick of his wrist. 'Mandy does it the whole time.'

'Mandy's different,' said Jimmy.

'That is undeniable,' said Ivor, 'but something must have upset you, Stephanie?'

'Yes. That bottle' – a quivering forefinger indicated which bottle – 'has got some revolting chemical in it and Kelvin is going to poison the pool with it.'

'Good Lord! You can't, Kelvin. You'll ruin one of the best pools on the river and could do all sorts of damage to the fishing further down. I can see why you're upset, Stephanie.'

'I wasn't thinking of the fishing. I'm thinking about the environment.'

'Oh yes, the environment. Quite right. It is a worry. Still, I've always thought that we've got quite a lot of it hereabouts, haven't we?'

Stephanie's lips tightened. 'It's that sort of complacency that leaves room for Kelvin's vandalism.'

'Your eyes don't half flash when you're angry,' said Jason with admiration.

'Stop dripping on me, Jason!' During his return across the river, Jason had encountered a submerged rock upon whose encrustation of weeds his rubber boot had slipped. 'We're agreed that Kelvin cannot use his noxious substance in the river, anyway, Ivor?'

'Oh yes, most certainly. We can't have that sort of thing.'

Kelvin grunted in exasperation. 'Look. We're not here for fun. We're here to get rid of that fish before it does any more damage.'

'Yes, I know that. But we're going to have to do it without killing everything in the river.'

Kelvin flung to the ground the gaff he was holding.

'Right. That's enough! I'm not having any more to do with it. I'll just sit on my arse and have a quiet smoke and you can work out what to do.' He retired to a fallen tree trunk in a huff.

'Has anyone any suggestions on what we do next?' asked Ivor.

'Get into the water. Find out where the thing is and catch it with a tail noose or gaff it,' said Bill.

'How can that be done? The pool's bottomless,' said the commander.

'It's not *that* bottomless,' replied Jimmy. 'I reckon there'll only be a few bits more than waist deep.'

'I don't understand,' said Malcolm. 'How can the pool be both waist deep and bottomless?'

'It's a bit like a miracle,' explained Ivor. 'We all know that water can be changed into wine, but you'd be a bit of a twit to expect champagne when you turned on your tap.'

'I think I see. Well, who's going in?'

'Jason,' said Ivor. 'He's already wet.'

'Yeah! I'll go. I'll have to take the gaff, though, Stephanie.'

'All right,' said she grudgingly. 'But be careful. You don't want to hurt anything with it.'

Jason stopped, perplexed, in the act of stepping into the water. He glanced at Ivor with a mute appeal.

'You do know what a gaff is for, Stephanie?' said Ivor.

'Of course I do!'

'Then you'll understand that Jason may find it difficult not to hurt the ferox.'

'Yes, but I insist that he does his best not to cause unnecessary suffering.'

'Don't you worry,' called Jason, stepping into the water. 'I'll stick it in its belly real careful, just like you say.'

The spectators crowded the bank to watch Jason feel his way carefully out into the pool, using the long-handled gaff to probe the bed of the river before him just in case it should shelve suddenly towards the centre of the earth.

In the middle of the pool, gently awash, lay a huge mound of bedrock, covered in a thick layer of moss. The main flow of the river tumbled past on the east side of the rock while only a few terminal wisps of foam disturbed the tranquillity of the depths to the west. Most of the river bed was scoured rocks and pebbles, but here flood water had dropped some of its burden of soil and gravel to create a soft, sandy bottom.

'Go over to the rock in the middle!' ordered Kelvin. 'There's a ledge about a yard under the surface. You can get half a dozen salmon under it when they're running. I bet it'll be there.'

'It's bloody cold!' complained Jason. The water was at that most uncomfortable of levels where it just caressed the base of his scrotum. 'Why should the thing be under the ledge, anyway? There's a hell of a lot of pool.'

'It's meant to be some kind of a trout. Not a Dover bloody sole that's going to bury its head in the sand!' Kelvin shook his head sadly. 'I don't know what's up with the kids these days. I think it's television that's made them so ignorant. That Jason tried to sell me half a dozen pheasant eggs the other day, thinking they were chickens'!'

Most of his listeners looked surprised and shocked. If not of local poaching stock, they were dedicated pheasant killers whenever the opportunity presented itself.

Stephanie and Malcolm exchanged a furtive glance and did their best to look shocked as well.

'What a silly mistake! Imagine!' said Stephanie.

The water was now scouring the fluff out of Jason's belly button. He twisted back towards the shore, eliciting a roar from Kelvin.

'Where do you think you're going? Get out to that rock!'

'Who's looking after the net? If I stir something out and it makes a run for it, I'll be bloody pissed off if the thing gets away! I'm not going to freeze for nothing.'

Kelvin looked irresolutely towards the net. 'He's right, you know,' he growled. 'He didn't fix it to the bottom. It'll be flapping like a plastic rick sheet under the water. Malcolm, you don't have rheumatism yet. You go.'

Malcolm demurred. 'I haven't got any gumboots.'

'Don't matter, the water'd be over them anyway. Take off your trousers and get in.'

'No,' said Malcolm.

Ivor laughed. 'I bet you're frightened. You think you're Captain Hook and that ferox is the crocodile.'

'I forbid you to go into the water, Malcolm,' said his wife. 'You go, Ivor.'

'No fear!'

'Somebody's got to go!' said Kelvin.

'I'm coming out!' shouted Jason.

'Bugger it,' said Kelvin, looking round for inspiration.

Inspiration was strolling along the path above him. A tourist couple, out for an afternoon's walk, had paused to watch. They had an undisciplined Alsatian wheezing and prancing against its collar at the end of a short leather leash.

'You!' said Kelvin, pointing the remaining gaff at the man.

He jumped and the dog's hackles rose.

'Me?' said the man nervously and his wife, in a pale yellow anorak and light blue slacks, clutched at his arm.

'Yes, you! Would you like a drink?'

'A drink?' The tourist looked round at the trees with a wild surmise. 'Where?'

Kelvin frowned. 'Where? Here, of course. I'm offering you some whisky.'

Delving into his pack, he produced a battered pewter flask, made a century earlier to carry cider into the fields to sustain lunching peasants, and waved it enticingly.

The tourist looked irresolutely at the flask, at Kelvin and at the other hunters.

His wife tugged at his arm. 'I don't think you should, dear.'

A calculated snort of contempt from Kelvin proved to be effective coarse psychology as it shamed the tourist into action.

He squared his shoulders. 'Hold Rajah, dear.'

'Where do you think you're going, Lionel?'

'Lionel's going to have a little drink, aren't you, Lionel?' said Kelvin. 'You just hold Rajah, missus, like Lionel says and don't you worry your pretty little head about anything.'

Missus was short and had a face like a worried toad. In her thirty years of life, her head could rarely have been called pretty. She blushed, further misting the heavy-framed spectacles that magnified her prominent eyes. Her husband was about ten years older than her with greying hair which hugged his head in closely controlled waves.

'What are you up to?' Jason said to Kelvin.

'This'll only take a minute. You can get back into the water,' he replied as Lionel slid down the hill to the river bank. The high heels of his cowboy boots cut a furrow through the loose earth.

Kelvin smiled at him, exposing his plastic teeth in a grin that would have alarmed an incoming Exocet.

He put an arm round Lionel's shoulder. 'It's wonderful to have a chance to meet you, Lionel.' Lionel essayed a weak grin as Kelvin massaged his shoulder beneath his black leather bomber jacket. 'You're in luck today!'

'Am I?'

'I'll say you are. You're going to have something to tell your friends about. Do you know what day it is today?'

'Sunday, isn't it?'

'It's St Stephanie's day, and every tenth St Stephanie's day we hunt the ferox round here. Very, very few outside have ever participated in a ferox hunt. But you're in luck!'

'Me?'

'Yes, you. Have a drink!'

He had little choice. Kelvin lifted his flask to the area of Lionel's mouth and upended it, leaving him a choice between drinking or dribbling. He coughed.

The rest of the locals watched with reluctant respect. Jason, moving back into the shallows, paused to follow the exchange.

'Why me?' asked Lionel.

That was a bit of a poser which Kelvin sidestepped.

'The ferox hunt is one of our oldest rituals. I bet you're wondering what the ferox is, aren't you?'

'Well, now you mention it . . .'

'It's a fish! But no ordinary fish. The BBC tried to film the hunt ten years ago for the television but royalty was present and they didn't want no publicity.'

'Royalty? Did you hear that, dear?'

Dear had been struggling down the slope in her husband's wake. 'I heard it. Don't you listen to a word the man says! It's time we were getting home. Rajah wants his tea and you haven't finished the grouting in the bathroom. What sort of royalty?'

The royal family has a member to suit everybody. The Princess of Wales was the obvious candidate for Dear, but she was too recent an accretion to the institution to serve Kelvin's purpose. His decision was further complicated since Lionel would probably best identify with Philip or Andrew, but it was Dear who had to be won over.

'The Queen Mother,' he said, firmly. 'God bless her.'

'Gosh!' said Dear. 'What did she do?'

'Her Majesty was Mistress of the Net.' He brandished the gaff. 'This is the very instrument with which she caught the 1976 ferox. They all belong to the Crown, you know, like sturgeons and pillarboxes. Being Master or Mistress of the Net is the greatest honour of all in a ferox hunt. The last ordinary person to do it was the Duke of Exeter.'

'Gosh!' repeated Dear. 'They won't believe me when I tell them about it at work tomorrow.'

'What can I do?' asked Lionel eagerly. 'Me in the ferox hunt, dear! And we nearly went to your mother's today instead!'

Kelvin looked at the tourists with satisfaction and smirked at the others. 'Well, we might as well get on with it, then.'

'Thank God for that!' said Jason. 'Have we sorted out who's going to get on the net then?'

'We have to follow the traditional ceremony,' stated Kelvin.

'Do we?' said Ivor faintly. 'Tell us about it, Kelvin.'

Kelvin frowned. 'I was just about to. We now auction the Mastership of the Net as usual – for charity, of course.'

'Of course,' said Ivor.

Kelvin clapped his hand to his forehead. 'Heavens! We've got a stranger here. Damn! And I was hoping for the net myself this year!'

Ivor looked resignedly at Bill. The latter shrugged.

'What do you mean?' asked Lionel.

'It's the tradition that a stranger's bid is always worth double that of a native of Moorcombe. If, for example, one of us bids . . . er . . . £40, then the stranger can Keep the Net for £20. But you wouldn't do that, Lionel, would you? You don't want the net.'

'£20! That's a lot of money!'

'The Queen Mother paid £21. That's 'cos royalty has to bid in guineas.'

'I thought they didn't carry any money,' said Dear.

Kelvin laughed. 'Of course they don't! Her lady-in-waiting filled out a cheque for her. Her Majesty's cheque card number was 2. I bet the Queen's is 1. She's expected here in '96.'

Rajah stopped pulling against the leash in Dear's hand. Sitting down, he cocked a leg and began to lick his genitals.

'Have you got £20, dear?' asked Lionel.

'I was saving all my cash for tea but I've got a cheque book.'

'Cheques are only acceptable from royalty,' said Kelvin promptly. 'You'll get a free cream tea in the village later. The Master of the Net always gets a free cream tea.'

Lionel scrabbled through his wallet. Dear did the same with her handbag. They came up with a few notes and a fistful of coins.

'There's only £19 here,' said Lionel. 'We really have to keep back £1 for emergencies. Is £18 enough?'

'£18. Right. I bid £36. Going, going, gone.'

Kelvin neatly relieved Lionel of the money. 'You are the Keeper of the Net. Let's get on with it. OK, Jason!'

68

Lionel and Dear exchanged an excited glance. 'What do I have to do?' asked Lionel.

'Get in the water and make sure that net at the end of the pool doesn't come adrift in the current.'

'What? I'll ruin my trousers!'

'If Her Majesty can hitch up her skirt, you can roll up your trousers.'

'Come on! Get on with it!' shouted Jason.

'Hurry up, Lionel. Don't be so wet!' said Dear, earning a snort of laughter from many of the natives. 'I'll hold your trousers.'

Removing his trousers, the unfortunate Lionel gingerly entered the river.

'That was a remarkable achievement, Kelvin,' said Ivor, watching Lionel's spindly urban shanks disappear beneath the water.

Kelvin flashed a mischievous grin. 'Bloody marvellous, isn't it? So long as we can keep the daft bugger at it.'

Lionel's feet slipped on a rock. He thrust down an arm to save himself, uttering a cry of distress as he wet his leather jacket.

'Your Lionel's doing just grand, missus,' said Kelvin. 'That's the Duke's Rock, he's slipped on. Named after the old Duke of Gloucester in the '36 Hunt. He fell there too.'

Lionel secured the net round the Duke's Rock and began to complain. 'I think I've cut my foot on a broken bottle.'

'Stay where you are, then!' bellowed Kelvin cheerfully. 'Cold water's just the thing for a cut. The 1886 ferox took the arm off Lord Nelson. Didn't do him any harm, did it?'

Having returned to the central rock, Jason was rootling around beneath the surface with his gaff to find the ledge.

'If there's not a salmon or two under there, I'll eat my socks!' said Kelvin.

Cries of disgust came from those that knew his socks.

'For God's sake!' exclaimed Stephanie. 'There are limits – even for you!'

'I can't feel a thing with this gaff,' yelled Jason. 'I'm going to stick my arm under.' He gave an exclamation. 'Christ it's cold!'

The spectators held their breath.

'Ah! There's something here!'

A sigh of satisfaction ran along the river edge.

'Get ready, Lionel, in case it makes a run for it.'

Hopping up from the rock on which he had been sitting to examine his foot, Lionel stood, peering into the pool.

Jason suddenly disappeared beneath the surface, emerging a few seconds later. 'Chuck us over your bottle, Kelvin. I'm never going to get anywhere with the gaff!'

Kelvin had the plastic container of poison sailing through the air before anyone could stop him.

'Kelvin! What do you think you're up to?' shouted Stephanie, rising to her feet.

'Hold your peace, woman! He's only going to put a bit round the ledge. It's the only way we'll ever winkle the beast out unless you prefer dynamite.'

'Well, I object. Most strongly. Ivor, you ought to do something.'

'Er . . . you'll only use a little bit, Jason?' called Ivor.

'Oh yes! Just a trickle. I'll just take the top off under the ledge and let a tiny bit out.'

'I think we ought to let Jason do as he thinks fit,' said Ivor. 'After all, we are chasing a rather dangerous creature. Just a little bit, Jason.'

'I'm very shocked,' said Stephanie, moving right to the edge of the river to watch as Jason plunged the container beneath the water to the length of his arms.

'Be prepared, Lionel!' shouted Kelvin. 'I should think the stuff will only knock the fish out. It won't kill them.'

Raising a hand in acknowledgement, Lionel sploshed along the 20-yard length of his net to ensure that it was ferox-proof.

Jason lifted the bottle back out of the water with the top firmly screwed back into place.

They waited.

The chiff-chaffs stopped chiff-chaffing and the warblers stopped warbling. The wind, which had been soughing through the trees at the top of the wood, died.

Rajah stopped licking his rude bits.

Bill uttered a cry: 'Look!'

All were already looking.

Breaking the surface of the black water of the pool, were the first bellies, two of them. Typical of the river, they were brown trout

70

weighing in at rather less than ½ lb apiece. Floating lazily in the current, they drifted gently towards the net.

A dozen pairs of eyes continued to sweep the water.

Stephanie squeaked.

A tail broke the surface, only to subside again before the bulk of its owner wallowed into view. It was a salmon this time, a reasonable fish of 6lb or so.

'That's a bit more like it!' said Kelvin with satisfaction. 'I'd have hoped for a bit more, mind you.'

'That's not the ferox,' said Ivor. 'Nor's that,' he added as another very similar salmon showed itself.

'Not to worry,' said Kelvin. 'I haven't cleared this pool for years and those are both nice clean fish.'

'But they're not feroxes.'

Kelvin looked at him curiously.

'You didn't really believe there was some monster in here,

did you? You should know better. I thought you just wanted to find out what was there. I get like that myself.'

'Ah!' said Ivor who had been more interested in the water than Kelvin's conversation. 'Now that's a ferox!'

Kelvin's head swivelled back to the pool, his jaw dropping with amazement. 'Christ! What the hell is that?'

The fish took a different path from the others. Drifting round the edge of the rock, it rotated lazily in an eddy.

The locals were in much the same state of shock as Kelvin. They watched in silence as Jason waded towards it and peered from a distance of about 10 feet. 'It's not a salmon!'

'It must be a salmon,' muttered Bill.

'Yes. There's got to be damn near 15lb of it,' agreed Kelvin.

'It's the ferox,' said Ivor. 'I'm telling you, I saw it take a duckling. No salmon would ever do that.'

Jason pulled out a stick from some flood wrack wedged into a crevice on the rock and gave the fish a careful prod, making it dip out into the current to begin its stately progress towards the net.

Jimmy shook his head in wonderment. 'I've fished this river man and boy and I've never seen anything like it.' He raised his voice. 'Make sure you get that fish all right.'

The first trout had already floated into the net and Lionel was wading carefully towards them. He saw the first salmon hit the mesh, changed his mind and began to splash back towards it. Then the second hit and, finally, the ferox.

They all met the mesh within 10 yards on the spectator side of the river.

The net had already been under some pressure due to the speed of the current. The 15lb of the ferox was too much for its anchorage on the far side of the river.

Stephanie was first to see the impending catastrophe.

Her cry of warning came as the net broke loose from the tree root to which Jason had secured it. Lionel hurled himself, black leather jacket and all, into the water to grab the loose end.

He emerged, spluttering, from the water holding the end of the net. Securing it to the Duke's Rock, he looked proudly to the bank for applause.

It came. Unstinting.

'Well done!' shouted the commander.

'Thank God!' exclaimed Kelvin fervently. 'It would have been a tragedy if we'd lost the fish. Bring it in to this bank, Lionel! You're a grand Net Keeper!'

Towing the net behind him with the fish embraced in its folds, Lionel waded towards the bank. The locals crowded round as he beached it while Rajah pulled Dear down to the water's edge in order to enjoy a sniff.

Everyone peered at the ferox. The fish were waking up to thrash in the mesh, demonstrating Jason's restrained use of Kelvin's bottle.

'It's a rainbow! A bloody great rainbow trout!' exclaimed Ivor. 'How on earth did it get in here?'

'It's enormous!' said Kelvin with awe. 'There's only one place it could have come from. The fish farm. It's only a mile and a half down river.'

'But there aren't trout that size there.'

'There are. He's got a pondful of submarines that he uses as breeding stock. One must have escaped when the river flooded after that thaw in February.'

'Well done, Lionel,' said his Dear. 'We'll have the big one for tea next Saturday when Wally and Jean come round with the children.'

Kelvin turned to her like a wolf. 'What are you talking about?' he snarled 'It's going to be stuffed and shoved above the bar.'

'My Lionel caught it and he's paid £18 for it and we're having it. He's ruined his jacket and that cost £33.20 in the January sales. You can have one of the little ones.' She pointed at the salmon.

'Little ones? There's £20's worth there!'

'In that case you've had rather a good afternoon. My Lionel was Keeper of the Net and he gets first choice.'

'The Keeper of the Net gets bugger all!' said Kelvin.

'Nonsense!' said Dear. 'You're not pretending that the Queen Mother didn't get to keep the ferox last time? If she did come at all! And I don't think it's very likely that she did what Lionel did.'

Kelvin turned a nasty shade of red.

'Oh look!' said Stephanie, changing the subject.

'What?' growled Kelvin, tearing his eyes from Dear who had

sensed enough of his hostility to shorten Rajah's lead, drawing the animal closer for protection.

'The river!'

There was a happy cry from the water. 'Afternoon!'

'Bugger me!' said Kelvin with scorn.

Sliding down the chute that entered the top of the pool was the first of a string of half a dozen canoes.

This particular manifestation of urban man as tourist was not popular in the locality. Nothing was more guaranteed to curdle the milk of human kindness in a fisherman than to watch a string of such canoes cross a river pool to which he had stalked on his belly to avoid scaring the fish.

The pilots of this particular flotilla were wearing yellow crash helmets and life-jackets. It was a school party. All save the leader with beard and goggles were teenagers, two with pop music emerging from the covered bowels of their kayaks.

Kelvin's lip curled in contempt.

The leader raised his paddle in the air. 'Afternoon!' he called once more.

'Get out of here!' yelled Kelvin. 'Bloody yobbos! Haven't you anything better to do with your time?'

Secure in the knowledge that they were being swept rapidly downstream by the current, this elicited a chorus of raspberries and a waving of digits from the group.

One small youth at the tail of the fleet skimmed towards the bank, plunging his paddle into the water, sending an arc of spray towards the spectators.

'You cheeky little bastard!' shouted Kelvin, searching round for an appropriate stone with which to show his disapproval of such conduct.

'Piss off, grandad,' replied the youth, sneering over his shoulder.

Showing that his heart was in the right place, Rajah plunged on his lead and barked.

Lionel had brought the half of the net to the bank, but the rest was still strung out to the Duke's Rock. The other canoes had avoided it, but the sneerer was in a hurry to escape any missile from Kelvin.

He caught it on his bows as he raced through.

The net left the shore in a hurry.

Kelvin, who had been standing on a portion of it, fell heavily into the shallows. In spite of another valiant dive by Lionel, the net and its contents were whisked into the river.

The cries of rage and distress torn from a dozen throats galvanized the youth into frantic paddling. He, the net, two trout, two salmon and a ferox tore through the rapids at the end of the pool and on down the river.

The bulk of the net was found two pools further downstream where its hijacker had paused to disentangle it from his canoe.

There was one salmon still enfolded in its nylon embrace but, filleted and pulped by the passage between canoe and rocks, it was good for nothing but fish fingers.

The ferox was never seen again.

Chapter Five

Butterfly

'WHAT'S HE up to now, then?' asked Kelvin, wriggling his naked toes luxuriously in the warmth of the sunshine.

It was Bank Holiday Monday, Mandy's birthday. She had invited the establishment of Moorcombe down to celebrate. Opposite their cottage, the river ran on the other side of a low stone wall in front of which she and Keith had placed white garden chairs.

Kelvin had strung an electric fence across the entrance to the lane to discourage the tourists. Milling aimlessly in the street between the church and the bridge, they were looking for the opportunity to spend money on postcards and ice creams. Both the café and the post office had discovered that tourists were driven by the need to spend money like dogs by the need to mark a lamp post. They catered for this atavistic urge with shelves of plaster pixies, plastic stags and cheap tin trays.

Safely ensconced behind the fence, a line of natives sat with their feet on the wall, enjoying the perfect summer afternoon. Hatching caddis flies, launching themselves from the long grass on the far side of the river, ran the gauntlet of rising trout, skimming swallows, martins, fly-catchers and wagtails. Survivors were finally picked off by the screaming squadrons of swifts, patrolling above the tops of the trees, blowsy in billowing green, on the hillside opposite.

'What's who up to?' asked Malcolm, sipping from his glass and placing it back on the wall.

'Archie, of course,' said Kelvin. 'The bugger runs like a rabbit whenever I try to see him.'

'I don't blame him,' said the commander, 'He probably

reckons you want to beat him up rather than simply rip him off.'

'He's up in London a lot trying to sell his business,' said Bill, 'but he was there when I went to look at the cattle on Friday. He's full of schemes.'

'What sort of schemes?'

'Every bloody thing. He's going to make the farm into a country park and put up benches and tables for picnickers. Or he's going to cover the land in bungalows. Or build a motor racing circuit or a golf course. I won't get the grazing for another season, that's for sure anyway. Pity, really.'

'Did he talk about Brett? Prudence won't even say if she's seen him yet.'

'He didn't mention Prudence or Brett. He's gone back to London, now.'

'Damn!' said Kelvin.

'He's certainly got pots of money,' said Keith. 'He's got some chap down who's tarting up the house. It's costing him thousands.'

'It's bad that,' said Jimmy. 'You should have got the job, Keith. You and Jason. Not some outsider.'

'To be fair, he did ask me to quote, but he was in a hell of a hurry. We'd got Frank Mattock's new chicken house to finish and then we'd promised Jason's father new seats for their privy.'

'Woodworm, eh?' said Kelvin.

'That's right.'

'I had woodworm in mine a few years back. Bloody shame. It takes years and years to get a really comfortable natural polish. Double seater, is it?'

'Yes.'

'Oak, that's the thing. Ash gets a bit ridgy after a while.'

A goggle of tourists paused on the far side of the river. Kelvin bared his teeth in a snarl. They hurried on.

'I heard that Archie was thinking of making the farm into a nature reserve,' said Stephanie. 'I think it would be wonderful.'

Kelvin snorted. 'It's one already. There hasn't been any decent farming done there for fifty years.'

'Sounds like your place,' said Bill.

Kelvin, surprisingly, laughed. 'Seriously, though, the last thing we want is any more of these bloody naturalist types wandering round. One like you is quite enough, Stephanie!'

'Is that meant to be amusing, Kelvin?' asked Stephanie.

'It's all right. I don't mean no harm to you, my dear. Decorative, that's what you are. Decorative. It don't matter if a head as pretty as yours is full of nonsense.'

Stephanie looked stonily out across the river. She no longer bothered to argue with Kelvin.

Feeling that his marital duty demanded it, Malcolm protested. 'Come on, Kelvin. There's nothing wrong with naturalists.'

'Nothing wrong? Do you remember Parson Brown from Beazelford?'

'Bugger me, yes!' exclaimed Bill. 'I haven't thought about him for years. He used to wander round with a net chasing butterflies.'

'That's him,' said Kelvin. 'He called himself a leopard something or other. I lost two cattle because of him.'

'Lepidopterist,' supplied Stephanie.

'Yes. He used to trespass all over the farm after his bloody butterflies. Couple of times I nearly shot him thinking he was a deer when he was crashing away in the woods or behind a hedge. All these tourists are bad enough without having the place infested with naturalists.'

'I don't remember him coming near Northcott,' said Bill.

'No, I tackled him once about why he was always in our top field. I said he ought to stay in his own bloody parish but he said some little butterflies up there were special.'

'They killed him, didn't they?' said Bill.

'That's right, it was a bad business.'

'He was killed by butterflies?' asked Stephanie, incredulous.

'If he hadn't been chasing them, he would still be alive today,' replied Kelvin.

'Oh, he was the chap struck by lightning, wasn't he?' said the commander.

'That's right. In my top field. The bolt went straight through him and killed two of my bullocks. The only reason they were there was that they were curious, wanting to know what he was up to. If the bugger hadn't been there, nor would my bullocks.'

'Do you remember what sort of butterflies they were, Kelvin?' asked Stephanie.

Draining his glass, Kelvin belched. 'It ain't bad beer this, Keith.'

'Would you like some more?'

'Well, that would be very civil of you.'

Taking the glass, Keith crossed the road and went into the cottage. Kelvin watched benignly. 'Obliging sort of chap, Keith.'

'What sort of butterflies were they, Kelvin?' repeated Stephanie.

'Blue, they were. The parson dragged me up to show me once.'

Stephanie frowned. 'There's lots of blue butterflies round here.'

'I know. I think he was tenpence in the shilling.'

'Do you remember anything else about them?'

Kelvin looked puzzled. 'I told you. They were butterflies, just blue butterflies. There's nothing else to say about them. They didn't use to do much except flap around looking pretty.' His face suddenly brightened. 'Oh yes! He had some daft story about them living in ants' nests.'

'When was this, Kelvin?'

He looked at her curiously. 'What's so interesting about blue butterflies?'

'It's just a thought, but they sound as if they might have been the large blue and they haven't been on the British list for a decade.'

Kelvin shrugged. 'Well, you can't ask Parson Brown. He got killed twenty-five years ago, I suppose. 'Bout then, wasn't it, Bill?'

'How long's the new parson been over at Beazelford?' asked Bill.

''Bout twenty-five years, I suppose.'

'Kelvin'll be right then, Stephanie. Because the new parson went there after Parson Brown was killed. A parson killed by a bolt from heaven. There were a few laughs about it at the time, I can tell you!'

'I was never lucky enough to see a large blue,' said Stephanie. 'They'd gone before I had the chance.'

A damsel fly, wings an irridescent blue-green, landed on the well. Leaning forward, Kelvin extended a casual thumb and crushed it. 'I wouldn't say this to everybody, Stephanie, but if you like you can come round next week some time and I'll show you them.'

'What?' Stephanie's voice rose to a shout.

'Keep your hair on, my dear. I'll only show you the butterflies. I won't do anything else.'

Mandy laughed. 'You wouldn't be much to worry about.'

'What do you mean? If I felt like it, she'd have lots to worry about. I'm not that old and she's a fine-looking woman.'

'It's true,' said Bill. 'When you go out jogging, my dear, all that bouncing around gets even Jimmy a bit excited.'

'I can't deny it,' said Jimmy.

'I've long admired them, myself,' said Keith, walking carefully up bearing a brimming glass for Kelvin.

Stephanie was thinking of something else.

'Kelvin, you're talking nonsense. The large blue doesn't exist any more. It's extinct in this country.'

'Is it? Perhaps somebody ought to tell the butterflies, then. Certainly the things Parson Brown used to run after are still getting on with their own business where they always have been. In fact I was up at the top a couple of days ago and I hit three of them with my stick. I've got a good eye still. It's not everybody who can knock a butterfly out of the sky with a stick. I can do it to bumblebees as well.'

'It can't possibly be large blues.'

'You're probably right, my dear. P'raps they're just medium blue or even an itty-bitty blue. 'T'ain't a very big butterfly. Not like a red admiral. Daft old bugger, Parson Brown. He most probably got it wrong.'

'Even so, I'll pop up and take a look.'

'You'd be most welcome.'

'I'll come too,' said Keith.

'You bloody well won't!' said Kelvin. 'I want you all to myself, Stephanie. Pop in when you're out for a jog. That'll be nice. Good healthy sweat's most becoming in a maid, especially when she ain't no maid any more.'

'I sweat sometimes,' said Mandy.

'Becoming on most maids, anyway.'

The following Sunday, the village cricket team was playing at home on Kelvin's field. It was not one of the three key matches played against neighbouring villages but the annual clash between church and chapel: Church of England versus Noncomformist.

Before the war it had been a serious fixture. Grave umpiring problems were only resolved when the squire could persuade a local Catholic grandee and his house priest to volunteer. These days it was more relaxed. Umpiring was now the job of the batting team and some of the players had never voluntarily entered a house of worship in their lives. However, once an incomer had become a cricketing piskey or methody, it was a life-long commitment.

For three seasons the Established Church had had a run of success, but the Dissenters had more of a chance this year. The Episcopalian star player, a founder member of the commune on the edge of the parish, was absent, battling with police over the right to worship the sun at Stonehenge during the summer solstice.

Sitting out in a deckchair in the shade of a hedgerow oak with a cup of tea by her side was Stephanie. She had been playing tennis up at the manor and had come down to show support for Malcolm, captain of the Chapel team. She was wearing her badminton kit.

Keith and the commander, both tail-end batsmen for the

Church of England, were sitting on the grass at her feet from where they could best admire her sturdy brown thighs beneath her short white skirt.

Cries of outrage from the field distracted them.

Having come through the gate on the opposite side of the field, Kelvin was walking straight across the cricket square. He paused between the batsmen for an altercation with Dennis, umpire at the bowler's end, before continuing his passage towards Stephanie's thighs.

'Hot, isn't it?' he said, removing his cap to use it as a mop for his brow.

'It would be cooler if you weren't wearing a tweed jacket,' said Stephanie.

'I took it off in 1976 in the drought and I got toothache. So I keep it on now when it's hot and I'm fine.'

'What was all that about?' asked the commander, indicating the players with a jerk on the thumb.

'Silly buggers!' replied Kelvin. 'It's my bloody field. I'll walk across it when I like!'

Shading her eyes from the sun, Stephanie looked up at Kelvin. Keith groaned in appreciation as her movement tightened the fabric of her T-shirt across her chest. 'I was thinking of looking you up, Kelvin.'

'Now that's what I call a coincidence! I'm here to see you. I've brought down the remains of one of those butterflies 'cos I knew you were interested.'

Stephanie sighed. 'I wish you'd stop killing the things, Kelvin.'

'Why? It's just an insect. There are millions of them.' Fumbling inside his jacket pocket, Kelvin extracted a scrap of newspaper, handing it over to Stephanie. 'I got the butterfly in here. If it's one of the extinct kind, we can go and see them.'

He looked speculatively at her legs.

'There's a patch of nettles, but I can carry you over them.'

'I've got a tracksuit in the car,' said Stephanie. Sitting up in the deckchair, she placed the scrap of newspaper in her lap and carefully unfolded it. She caught her breath.

'I don't believe it!' she said, examining the mangled remains of a small blue butterfly. 'It is! It's a large blue!'

'Are you going to come up then?' asked Kelvin eagerly.

Stephanie was not listening. 'A large blue! I'm the only person in the country who knows that the large blue is not extinct.'

'I brought another one in case I mashed that one in my pocket,' said Kelvin, pulling out another scrap of newspaper. 'I got them both an hour ago with my stick.'

'If your eye's that good, I don't know why you're not still playing cricket,' said the commander.

'He wasn't selected,' said Keith.

'I wouldn't buy Malcolm a drink!'

'It's a real live large blue,' said Stephanie. 'Kelvin . . .' She placed her hand on his arm.

'What is it? You're coming through the woods with me!'

'Kelvin, will you promise me something?'

'Promise you something?' A guarded expression crossed his face. 'What sort of something?'

'Will you promise me that you'll never, ever kill one of these butterflies again?'

Wheeling high in the blue sky above the cricket field, a buzzard screamed. The cawing rooks rose from their nests in the beech trees beyond the hedge to mob it.

'What's in it for me?' asked Kelvin. 'If I start promising you one thing, then you'll want another.'

'Kelvin, these are extremely rare.'

'So are warble flies. But I get fined if any of my cattle go to market showing warbles on their backs.'

'Kelvin . . .'

'And Colorado beetles. Now they're pretty little things, bit like ladybirds.'

'Kelvin,' said Stephanie, 'I hate to have to tell you this, but you've broken the law twice today already. These butterflies are protected. It's strictly against the law to kill this species of butterfly.'

'Oh! Good shot, sir!' said the commander.

Gerald Mowbray, a moorland farmer of mighty thews, had connected at last, sending a ball high above the bowler's head to land in the river which bounded the field.

Fishing in his pocket, Kelvin shook out another butterfly. He laughed.

'You're having me on! You said yourself these things are extinct and so they wouldn't have a law to protect something that's extinct. Show me the law which says I can't shoot dinosaurs or dragons or . . . or . . .'

'Unicorns?' suggested Keith.

'Yes. Or unicorns.'

'They were put under the protection of the law when there were still a few left.'

The commander's eyebrows shot up. 'Unicorns?'

'Large blues.'

'Huh!' grunted Kelvin. 'Well, I'm not making any promises.'

'It's the law, Kelvin,' said Stephanie.

'Bugger the law! They're on my land and it's nobody's business but my own.'

Stephanie decided to take action.

'Right! Right!' She rose to her feet, caught the direction of Keith's gaze and backed smartly away from her deckchair. She glared once more at Kelvin. 'We'll see about that!' She marched off towards the field gate.

'Cor! Look at them bounce!' said Keith.

'Where d'you think Stephanie's gone?' said Kelvin, looking lustfully towards the gate.

The commander rose to his feet but Kelvin was too quick.

'Is it still warm?' asked Keith as Kelvin sat down in the vacated deckchair.

'I expect she's gone to the lavatory,' said the commander through tight lips. 'Do you want a chair, Keith? The ground's getting a bit damp.'

'Thanks.'

The commander walked towards the horsebox which served as pavilion and tea tent. He had a word with other cricket watchers clustered in its shade, returning to the oak tree with two more deckchairs. He set them up.

'I hope Stephanie isn't going to be long,' said Keith.

'You'll have to give up your chair when she comes, Kelvin,' warned the commander.

'She can sit on the ground and get ants in her pants. She seems to love the bloody things.'

For fifteen minutes they watched the cricket. Ivor was batting at one end, missing ball after ball. At the other, Gerald Mowbray was hitting one in three, sending the balls flying over the boundary or high in the air to be dropped by the fielding side.

In the shade of the oak tree, Kelvin's head began to droop. He snored.

Heralded by a growl of lust from Jimmy by the horsebox, Stephanie returned. Behind her trailed a red-faced Percy Green, the local policeman. Only just regulation height, Percy was round and plump. He had bulging cheeks decorated by tufts of hair and a brace of shiny chins that disappeared into his shirt. He was not in uniform.

The commander looked up. 'Hullo, Percy. Why aren't you in your garden?'

'I was,' replied Percy shortly, 'till Stephanie told me about these here butterflies. Kelvin! Wake up!'

Kelvin opened a cautious eye.

'I looked up the law, Kelvin, and it's a very serious matter if you do anything to harm them.'

'Is that right?' said Kelvin.

He stretched and shaded his eyes to look out at the cricket. 'Oh, well hit, Ivor!'

The latter had finally made contact with one of the Dissenting balls and sent it hopping across the boundary.

'That's right,' confirmed Stephanie. 'You've got something unique at the top of your farm. The sooner we get some experts out, the sooner we can turn the area into a nature reserve where the butterflies will be able to have proper protection. Kelvin, you have no idea just how important this discovery is. It's going to be headline news!'

Kelvin turned his head towards Stephanie. 'Is that right?' he said again.

'Yes,' said Percy this time, 'that's right!'

Kelvin turned to the commander with a sigh. 'You see what I mean about conservationists now?' The commander nodded sympathetically. Kelvin turned to Stephanie and Percy. 'Can I have my say, now?'

'That colony of butterflies is so important that nothing you can say will change things,' said Stephanie.

Kelvin looked puzzled. He made sure he looked puzzled by knotting his brow in a ferocious grimace. 'What butterflies are you talking about?'

'This here butterfly,' said Percy, pulling a small blue corpse from his pocket. It was now contained in a polythene bag.

'Oh! That butterfly! I got it from my grandad's collection. I gave it to Stephanie as a little joke.'

'Kelvin!' Stephanie stamped her foot in rage.

'Very nice,' murmured Keith appreciatively as the shock waves of the stamp set her joggling.

Even Mandy would have been proud of the look that Stephanie sent him, but Percy spoke first. He lifted the plastic bag.

'If it came from your grandfather's collection, how come there's fresh goo from its guts all over the bag?'

Kelvin smiled. 'Oh, sorry. I meant a different butterfly. Which one's that?' Taking the bag from Percy's hand, he dropped it, trod on it and ground it into the grass.

'Oh, sorry,' he repeated. Picking it up, he pretended to examine it. 'It could be anything in there,' he said. 'What do you think, Commander?'

The commander peered at the bag. 'Yes. It could have been a butterfly, but now Kelvin's accidentally trodden on it, it could be anything.'

'Stop being so stupid! Where are the other two?'

'They got all scrunched up in my pocket,' said Kelvin, scrunching them up in his pocket.

'We'll just come and look over your farm till we find the colony, then,' snapped Stephanie.

Kelvin smiled serenely. 'There weren't ever butterflies like these on the farm. So you'd be wasting your time. Even if there had been, you wouldn't know where to look.'

It was Stephanie's turn to smile. 'The food plant of the large blue is wild thyme, so we only need to discover where it's growing and we've found the colony.'

'Clever,' remarked Kelvin approvingly, 'but I'm afraid I won't give you permission to go on my land.'

'Oh! Very good!' said the commander. Whether he was referring to Kelvin's remark or something happening out on the cricket square was unclear.

Stephanie was not finished. She laughed coldly. 'Ha! There are safeguards built in to the law to protect wildlife from people like you. We can force entry. All we need is a court order and we can go anywhere on your land that we like!'

Kelvin shook his head. 'I don't know what this country's coming to. Did you know about this 'ere law allowing riff-raff to trespass all over your land, Percy? Trampling the growing corn, aborting sheep and destroying fences?'

'I must admit I didn't,' replied the policeman uncomfortably. 'Not until Stephanie looked it up and pointed out. I've got copies of the laws at home, you see.'

'Wriggle out of that, Kelvin!' said Stephanie. 'Your attitude is a disgrace!'

Kelvin sighed. 'Look, missy. Why does the law say you can come on my land and meddle?'

'To protect the butterflies, of course!'

'That's right. For their protection. Now, if I had these butterflies like you say I have and they're the only ones there are left, why do you think that's so?'

'Well . . .'

Kelvin did not wait for her answer. 'I'll tell you why!' He

appeared genuinely moved. He certainly paused to readjust his top plate. 'It's because they've been left alone without any nosy parkers like you interfering with them! They've always been there and they always will be there so long as you buggers leave them be!'

'But . . .'

'But me no buts! Let me tell you something else. You go and get yourself a court order and you'll find that I've had to get Frank Mattock in to spray for aphids and there won't be no bloody butterflies no more. And I'll tell you another thing. If I even hear any more talk of interfering with those butterflies, then in comes Frank Mattock. What do you say to that, missy? Would you be protecting your precious butterflies by going to the law or would you be protecting them by telling Percy to go back to his marrows?'

Stephanie opened and shut her mouth but no words came.

Kelvin sniffed, turning his attention back to the cricket. 'But my invitation still stands. You come up with me to have a look and I'll lift you through the nettles. I won't kill no more of them either and you can keep an eye on them yourself, so long as you keep it a secret.'

Although torn by conflicting emotions, Stephanie was a pragmatist at heart. 'What about Percy? He's a policeman. He can't forget what I've told him.'

'Oh yes he can – can't you, Percy?'

Percy was bound to Kelvin by a decade of favour and counter-favour.

'I'm not on duty, I suppose. Not in uniform, anyway. And there hasn't been a crime committed since those there blue butterflies weren't those there blue butterflies at all.'

'See? It's all right now, Stephanie. I'm sure Prudence would love to have conservationizers in when I'm gone but, till then, let's just watch the cricket, eh?'

Her face scarlet, Stephanie stood in thought for a few seconds before turning on her heel and striding back towards the exit from the field. Percy trailed after her.

'But me no buts,' said the commander, looking at Malcolm running up to deliver a ball. 'Nicely put, Kelvin. Oh, well bowled, sir!'

Chapter Six

Candy

IN THE DINING ROOM of the manor, the squire was having his breakfast, moodily spooning rice crispies into his mouth while an ancient copy of *South West Farmer* was propped on the toast rack in front of him. It was opened at the centrefold which displayed a picture of Winston, his late Charolais bull.

He found the picture soothing. Even the wet rot, which he had discovered when he put his foot through the floorboards by the lavatory that morning, receded from the forefront of his mind to join the dry rot, the roof, the foundations and the cracks and crumbles to which he had become resigned.

A small man in his fifties with thinning hair, the squire had worn a moustache quite happily for most of his adult life. Then Mandy had told him that he looked like Groucho Marx. He now wore it less happily, particularly since he now had to wear spectacles.

His admiration for the way in which the photographer had caught the fullness of Winston's deliciously rounded rump was interrupted by the morning invasion of dogs. His wife, Marcia, bred miniature dachshunds which undulated ahead of her like a pack of yapping draught-excluders, pausing to copulate with, pee upon or bite anything that was unable to raise itself more than 8 inches above ground level.

The squire automatically lifted his feet from the floor to rest on the stretcher beneath the table as Marcia entered. Flushed from her early stint in the garden, she was carrying the mail.

'The roses are looking quite lovely,' she said, sitting down at the other end of the table. Pouring herself a cup of coffee, she began to open her letters.

The squire grunted, examining a final demand from the

district council. It was nothing to worry about. He was on the bench of the magistrate's court which sent summons for non-payment of rates round most of his friends.

He picked up a thick padded envelope with a word-processed address and a WC1 post mark. Wiping the butter knife on the sleeve of his sweater, he carefully slit the envelope and shook its contents on to the table. A fat paperback book and a letter slithered out. The squire frowned at them.

'Jane's youngest has just been posted to Canberra,' remarked Marcia. 'She's worried that he may forget to boil the water.'

Skimming his own letter, the squire grunted once more.

'Heavens!' he exclaimed with sudden excitement. 'Marvellous! Just what we needed! Callooh! Callay! I must call a meeting. The telephone! The telephone!'

He jumped up from the table, sparking an outburst of wheezy yaps from most of the dogs, and rushed from the room.

Catching the eye of the golliwog on the honey jar as she looked up, Marcia dipped her finger and absently licked it while she turned to the next page of her letter.

A couple of days after the arrival of the momentous letter, the squire held a meeting with influential citizens of Moorcombe in his library. A dozen of the local glitterati were present. Helping themselves to glasses of home-brewed beer, they made themselves comfortable in the scuffed, flaking leather chairs. The walls of the room were lined with shelves of books with scuffed, flaking leather bindings. The room smelled like an ancient grave, the air redolent with mildew and long-dead animals.

The squire knew his people and how to get their attention. He cleared his throat. 'I have a proposition here which could be worth £1000 to the community.'

Conversation died at once.

'It'll give us a wonderful start for the village hall fund. Isn't it marvellous?' The squire was sitting behind a large flat-topped desk inset with a patch of scuffed, flaking leather. Leaning back in the chair, he beamed happily at his audience.

'Is that all?' asked Lindy after a pause.

'Isn't that enough?' said the squire.

'Well, yes. As far as it goes. But it would be nice to hear a few details about how this miracle is going to take place.'

The squire nodded his head vigorously. 'Yes. I consider that a perfectly fair request.'

Raising their eyebrows, the glitterati looked at each other with resignation. There was little mystery about the squire's lack of success at making money.

'Well?' said Lindy.

'Oh, yes! Sorry.' The squire pulled an envelope from his inside pocket, sliding its contents on to the desk. He put on his spectacles.

'Now, this is a letter from my nephew in London who is a publisher. One of his writers was going to stay in a frightfully grand country house for a fortnight but the original host has cancelled and he wants me to be host instead. He's prepared to contribute £1000 to village funds.' The squire beamed. 'Good, isn't it?'

Ivor picked up the interrogator's baton. 'This is all very well.

But I'm sure your nephew's firm is not a charitable institution. They won't give away money just because this writer will be staying in the parish.'

The squire looked slightly hurt. 'It all seems quite straightforward to me. Guts, that's it.'

'I beg your pardon?'

'Guts,' repeated the squire.

'What have guts got to do with anything?' asked Ivor.

'That's the name of the writer.'

'Don't be absurd. Nobody is called Guts.'

The squire looked down at the letter. 'Its "G-U-T-Z". Candy Gutz. She's a she.'

'But why should she be worth £1000 to us?'

'She's an American,' explained the squire.

Jimmy drew in his breath.

The Cargo Cult had an enthusiastic following among the older members of the community. Never to be forgotten was the wealth of the GIs stationed just outside the village during the last part of the war.

'Apparently she writes what are known as blockbusters . . . er . . . ,' the squire looked down at the letter once more, 'towering sagas of human passion. Her next novel concerns an American female foundling who becomes a film star and marries an English duke.' The squire gave a slightly embarrassed smile. 'She then becomes president of America and finally saves the world by seducing the Russian prime minister.' The squire beamed. 'I'm sure it'll be jolly good.'

The company digested this information.

'Has she written any other books?' asked Lindy.

'At least one. It came with this letter.'

'What's it called?'

'I can't remember. Marcia is reading it, but it's at least 4 inches thick. There's a picture of a black woman wearing chains and very little else on the cover.'

'Not *Southern Spring*?'

'I'm not sure, I'm afraid. I picked it up but the first page was so astonishingly obscene that I didn't get any further.'

'It must have been *Southern Spring*. Yes, Candy Gutz. I think I saw her in a chat show. If it's her, she's blonde and fifty with jewels all over the place.'

'I've no idea what she looks like but she's coming here to do research on English country life for the bit where the heroine lives with the duke.'

Kelvin contributed to the conversation for the first time. 'If she's paying the village £1000, how much are you getting?'

The squire looked coy. 'I don't really think that is any of your business, Kelvin.'

'She must be rich, I suppose. So it must be a lot. £200 a week?'

The squire looked even more coy. 'My nephew tells me she's been given an advance of half a million dollars for this book.'

There was a stunned silence.

'What's an advance?' asked Kelvin.

'It's when you're given money before you actually write the book.'

'Half a million dollars for nothing!'

'It's not exactly nothing. She'll have to write the book.'

'Even so, half a million dollars! My dad wrote down everything he knew about ploughing with horses in an old exercise book. Do you think I could get money for that?'

'I doubt it,' said Lindy.

'Why?' said Kelvin, turning on her belligerently. 'It would make a bloody good book. He was second in the regional ploughing championships for two years running before the war. He was a very famous man. You're just ignorant. It's finished, too. Not like this Candy Gutz's book. I bet if I talked to her nice she'd tell me how to sell it.'

The assembly felt a twinge of pity for Candy Gutz. Being 'talked to nice' by Kelvin was a fate that many of them had had to endure, particularly when he had last campaigned for the parish council.

'I don't think that would be altogether wise,' said the squire, alarmed.

'Why not? What I get up to with Candy Gutz is between her and me.'

'Oh, quite,' agreed the squire hastily. 'However, we would like her to stay here for a full fortnight.'

'£500?'

'What?' asked the squire.

'£500 a week. What she's paying you.'

A smile of unbearable smugness played across the squire's lips. He stroked his moustache and adjusted the knot on his tie.

'It's a thousand!' exclaimed Kelvin. 'You jammy bugger!'

'How the hell did you know?' demanded the squire.

'You just told me.'

'You tricked me!' cried the indignant squire.

'That's right. 'Twarn't very difficult.'

'Right! For that you can't have any more beer!' Kelvin's face fell. Glasses had been drained and the drought was becoming serious. 'By the way,' continued his host, 'I'd be extremely appreciative if you would all keep that information to yourselves.'

'Of course,' murmured the commander, looking round the room and receiving insincere nods from everyone else. By asking for discretion, the squire had set the seal on a 22 carat item of gossip which would be common currency within a 10-mile radius half an hour after the meeting had broken up.

'Now, to get back to business . . .'

'If we keep it to ourselves, can we have more beer?' interrupted Kelvin.

'I suppose so.'

Glasses were refilled during the minute's interlude. The squire rapped the desk for order, raising a puff of leather dust as he did so. He sneezed violently, spending a busy 30 seconds trumpeting away into a red spotted handkerchief.

'Sorry about that. Now we have to work a bit for this money. She wants to stay in a typical country house and see life in a typical English village so that the settings are authentic for her book.'

'I've read one of her books,' volunteered Mandy. 'They had one in the mobile library but it was withdrawn because Mrs Baggins complained it was perverted. Candy Gutz is going to want to do more than just potter round your bullocks with you once a day.'

'I agree. I was about to come to that . . .'

'You're going to have to have it off with her in the shrubbery to show how the aristocracy do it,' said Kelvin with lip-smacking delight.

'I'll be damned if I will!'

Mandy smiled. 'In *Southern Spring* the heroine spent an entire

94

weekend in bed with a senator, the senator's grandmother and a set of bagpipes. At the very least, you're going to have to put on spurs and swing at her from the chandeliers.'

'The chandeliers wouldn't take it even if Marcia would. But if you would all shut up, I'll tell you what is needed.' As it was rare for the squire to assert himself, everyone shut up and prepared to listen. 'Now, it is not Miss Gutz who is going to pay this money. It is her publishers and they want her to see a very special sort of English way of life. It's got to suit the American market. Do I make myself clear?' He looked round the room.

Mandy was still spokesperson for the groundlings. 'No.'

The squire shifted impatiently in his chair. 'You're all being very slow. My nephew explained it very well.'

'Well, why not tell us what your nephew said?' suggested Ivor.

'That's a good idea. We have to provide Miss Gutz with the sort of England that she is expecting. It's no good showing it as it really is because that is not how Americans imagine it to be. My nephew specifically suggested that we put on a village fayre – that is, spelt with a "Y" like "tea shoppe".'

The meeting mulled this over.

Kelvin was not convinced. 'What are you going to be doing, then? It seems a bit unreasonable if we do all the work and you get twice as much money as everyone else put together.'

'I've got to turn on the central heating for a fortnight.'

'In the middle of August?'

'That's what I've been told. And I've got to hire a maid and a butler as well as buy a new suit of plus fours. Miss Gutz believes that all English gentlemen wear nothing but plus fours in the country. It's going to be awful.'

'Ah! But think of the money,' said Ivor.

Everyone thought of the money and it did help.

'What do you propose for the fayre?' asked Bill.

'That's the main reason I called this meeting. I hoped you might have some suggestions.'

The commander groaned. 'We'll have to have the morris dancers.'

'Over my dead body!' said Lindy. The rest of the room roared its agreement.

'It was just a thought,' said the commander.

'Keep thoughts like that to yourself,' said Ivor. 'How about getting the school children to sing songs?'

'Guessing the weight of a pig,' suggested Jimmy. 'I remember them doing that on *The Archers*.'

'I've got a better idea!' exclaimed Malcolm. 'Let's get them involved up at the commune. They're always going off to these summer festivals where they have troubadours, jugglers and people like that. It's just the sort of stuff we're after and they'd do all the organizing.'

'The communards?' said the squire uncertainly. 'Do you think that would be safe? You know what they're like. They are a little odd.'

'Safe? It would be marvellous! They'd do all the work for us and some of them are into the Olde Englysshe stuff. A couple of them are Druids at the moment, for a start. This Candy Gutz'll love it.'

'If you really think so.'

'I'm sure so. I'll get in touch with them once you give us the date.'

'All right. How about the third Saturday of the month? You Malcolm, Ivor and Lindy are in charge.'

'What about me?' demanded Kelvin, who liked to be at the centre of events providing no effort was involved.

'I have a role for you, Kelvin. I'm told this woman will be expecting a domestic staff. I thought you and the commander would make a splendid pair of gardeners.' Kelvin looked very dubious. 'I wouldn't expect you to actually do any gardening. Only that you would both be around to greet her. I thought we might have some sort of line-up of retainers when she arrives. I'm going to ask Archie Spontini to collect her from the station in his Range Rover.'

'I'd be the head gardener?'

'Of course. You wouldn't mind, Commander?'

'No, not at all. It would be a pleasure.' Being several generations removed from his bucolic forebears, the commander would have no difficulty with the masquerade. The memory of villeinhood was still too fresh in Kelvin's genes for him to play the part easily.

'Excellent! I think it's settled then. Let's fill our glasses to success and our profit.'

It was a toast worth drinking in champagne, but the cloudy dregs of the squire's beer provided a perfectly adequate substitute.

The promised arrival time was noon on Saturday. The welcoming committee was enjoying a glass of sherry in the sitting room of the manor when the dachshunds began to yap and seethe, giving early warning that a car was crunching up the gravel drive.

'Damn!' said the squire. 'Marcia! Where's Marcia?'

'You told her to go and put on a tweed suit and some pearls,' said Mandy. 'She's going to be far too hot, like me.'

The squire had decked Mandy out in a housemaid's uniform,

last used by Lindy in a production of *Hay Fever*. Being the larger of the two women, Mandy looked like a maturing strip artiste.

'Think of me in these blasted plus fours!' said the squire. 'See who it is, will you?'

'Go and find out for yourself,' said Mandy. 'I'm not a servant, even though I may look like one.'

'It's just that you are next to the window,' replied the squire mildly. 'I thought you might look through.'

'Oh, I see. All right, then.' Mandy teetered the few steps to the glass on high heels that made her resemble a hippopotamus in Disney's *Fantasia*. 'It's a Range Rover. They must be here.'

'Damn!' repeated the squire. 'Let's get down there.' Draining his sherry, he trotted out of the room, bellowing 'Marcia!'

The others followed.

The Range Rover was just pulling up outside the portico, added to the front of the house by an early nineteenth-century forebear of the squire, as the welcoming party spilled through the front door into the sunshine and formed itself into a rough line.

Archie was first out of the vehicle. Glancing nervously at Kelvin, he buttoned up his blue blazer and opened the back door.

Preceded by a blast of Chanel No. 5, Candy Gutz emerged into the sunshine, enormous sunglasses covering most of her face. She surveyed the scene.

The flaking golden stone of the manor house was swathed with Virginia creeper. In front of the building, the gravel lapped at the edge of the lawn on which the squire passed his Wednesdays, chugging up and down on his motor mower.

On the far side of the lawn lay a ha-ha which kept a bunch of creamy white Charolais heifers at a picturesque distance, and beyond them rolled the woods, fields and hedgerows of the soft green countryside up towards the purple heather of the moor.

'Gee!' said Candy. 'Ain't this the cutest thing?'

Petite was too soft a word for her. She had the muscular wiriness of the dedicated body worshipper, a California tan and a pale blue silk suit with American football shoulders. A great corona of blonde hair surrounded her head. Mandy gasped with admiration.

Clearing his throat, the squire stepped forward. 'Miss Gutz?'

'Candy, sweetie.'

'Sweetie?' repeated the squire blankly. He looked nervously round at the others but they were busy preserving the stolidity of the professional retainer. 'Er . . . I may have a toffee in my pocket.'

Candy raised her purple-tinged sunglasses to stare at the squire through startled brown eyes.

Ivor leaned forward. 'That's her name.'

'Oh! Of course. Ah! Candy, sweetie. I see. Very droll . . . er . . . let me introduce you to the staff.' He turned towards Ivor. 'This is my butler, Ivor, and these . . .'

He indicated Kelvin. The latter and his assistant, rather bashful in their smocks, had been practising forehead knuckling and forelock tugging for much of the morning. Having not quite mastered the technique, Kelvin was grimacing furiously as he punched his closed fist against his head.

But Candy was not yet finished with the squire.

'You are the squire?'

'Er . . . yes . . . that's right. Richard . . .'

'I'll call you Dickie.'

'Oh, will you?' replied the squire grimly. 'I'm not sure . . .'

Candy was not prepared to hear him out. Having labelled him 'Dickie', she was now ready to take in everyone else.

'And who are you?' she demanded, looking Kelvin up and down. 'Neat dress.'

In his enthusiasm for the forelock tug, Kelvin uprooted a substantial handful of hair which he could ill afford to lose. He bared his plastic teeth. 'Afternoon, missus. I be the head gardener.'

As a native, Kelvin already had a strong West Country accent. Having also been told that he had to play the country bumpkin, his words came out in slurred grunts.

'Gee,' said Candy uncertainly, 'are you British?'

'British!' exclaimed Kelvin, indignantly. 'I'm English. My family's been in this parish for as long as the squire's. And he don't count 'cos he's gentry.'

'Oh,' said Candy, looking to the squire for help in interpretation.

The commander moved smoothly forward to assist. 'Arr!' he said, touching his forehead with a finger. 'A very good morning to you, mum.'

Candy looked at him and then at Kelvin. She was not quite convinced.

'What's with you guys? Are you peasants or something?'

'I'm a peasant, mum. He's a yokel,' said the commander with relish.

'You're kidding!'

'No I'm not! Mangel worzel, arrr,' said the commander, striving for authenticity.

'Is that right? And I suppose you're going to tell me that you wear those dinky little nightshirts when you take out your plough horse?'

'Smocks, mum. Don't reckon much on horses these days. Oxen, them's the thing, 'cos you can eat them when they're too old to work.'

'Yeugh!' said Candy. 'That's a bit gross!'

Nudging the commander with his elbow, Kelvin gargled an impressive sounding sentence. It may have been intelligible at the local beast market a century earlier but not to anyone present.

'What?' asked the commander, bending his ear towards Kelvin.

'I said, we're supposed to be gardeners, you bloody fool. Not ploughmen.'

An expression of concern appeared on Candy's face. 'Gee! Is the poor guy disadvantaged?'

'What does that mean?' demanded Kelvin.

'Tenpence in the shilling,' the commander translated.

Candy had been listening with a cocked head. 'No, that's not English. Is he a member of an ethnic minority?'

'Damn cheek!' said Kelvin. 'I was talking perfectly normally. What's an ethnic minority?'

'Like Pakistanis and West Indians,' explained the commander.

'What! Is this horrible woman quite mad?'

'Gee! He's amazing! Can he understand me?' Displaying a set of eerily even teeth, she held out her hand to Kelvin. 'I'm very pleased to meet you, Yokel,' she said, enunciating her

words slowly and clearly. She turned to the squire, 'It's okay if I call him "Yokel", Dickie?'

'I didn't come here to be insulted, you stupid bloody woman,' snarled Kelvin.

'Er . . .' said the squire, wondering what he should do.

It was Mandy who came to the rescue. 'Madam,' she said.

Candy turned her smile from Kelvin to her. 'Candy, sweetie.'

'No, you misunderstand. I just meant that Madam is here to welcome you.'

Looking ill at ease in her tweed suit, Marcia slunk out from behind Mandy.

'Say!' exclaimed Candy. 'You're beautiful!'

It was quite true. Marcia was beautiful, although nobody had told her so since a Frenchman at a hunt ball in 1966. 'I just love your blue eyes and your complexion! You're a real English rose! What do you use for it?'

Marcia cast an agonized look at the others. She had donned her tweeds for the cause, but she had not been prepared for personal questions and compliments.

Candy came up to her, bracelets clanking. She took Marcia's hand in her own and stared at her face. Mothballs clashed with Chanel No. 5, the former retreating in the face of overwhelming odds.

'You look so young! Your surgeon must be a genius! He'd make a fortune back home!'

Marcia was lost. Her face, like every other face in the parish, was in debt to nothing save the rose-scented bars of blue soap sold loose in the cash-and-carry. She decided to ignore everything that Candy had said and start afresh.

'How do you do?' she said, pumping the hand that was still trapped between the rings on Candy's knuckles. 'You must be dying for lunch after your journey. Do come in. Such a lovely day, isn't it? London is simply hideous in this sort of weather.'

With one nervous glance over her shoulder to ensure that Candy was following, she babbled her way into the house.

Kelvin scowled after them. 'I've never been so insulted in my life. Stringy old hag! I've seen more meat on an old boiling fowl. Calling me a sambo! I'd a damn good mind to put her in her place!'

'She wouldn't have understood, even if you had done,' said the commander.

'I'm having nothing more to do with the cow! You can use my field for the fête, but keep her out of my sight!'

'Can we go now, Squire?' asked the commander.

'I want a word with Archie Spontini about Prudence first,' said Kelvin.

But Archie, having dumped a pile of suitcases on to the lawn, let in his clutch and sprayed gravel down the drive.

Early the following Friday morning, Kelvin was sitting on his well-polished circlet of oak at the bottom of the garden. He was admiring page 3 before putting her to good use. He shut his eyes and grunted, the paper falling against his pimply knees. But his concentration was interrupted.

His eyes opening wide, he cocked his head, listening intently. Ninety seconds later, tying the baler twine round his waist to keep his trousers up, he was scurrying up the weed-choked path to the house. The noise, a whisper of music, had died away, but Kelvin knew a trespassing trannie when he heard one.

He shouted for Prudence in the kitchen, but it was 8 am and she was ministering to a sheep whose lamb was unenthusiastic about entering a cruel world. Grabbing his shotgun from the umbrella stand by the door, he hurried off down the lane.

He was hoping for his favourite kind of trespassers. Ignorant of the law, they cowered together as he capered round them, spittle flecking his cheeks, while he ranted on about the temerity of those who dared set foot upon his land.

From the lane he hopped a wooden gate to run across a rushy field dotted with scrawny sheep that scuttled together for protection as their master appeared. Before plunging through the hedge into his flat field, he checked that he had cartridges in the breech of his ancient gun. He did not pull the hammers back to cock it because he had no wish to shoot anyone. Not by accident, anyway.

Many times had he plunged through the hedge in pursuit of cattle or tourists, but the sight before him was the stuff of his wildest nightmares. A cry of horror burst from his lips. Covering his field were tents of all shapes, colours and degrees of decrepitude, battered buses and vans painted with cabalistic shapes, signs of the zodiac and swirls.

He had forgotten about the fayre. All he saw was squatters. Half the vagabondage in the country seemed to have invaded his farm.

On the far side of the meadow a milling crowd of alternative campers were standing in the gateway, so he trotted across the field towards them, roaring with outrage at this invasion of his

territorial rights. He cut across the front of a colourfully daubed tepee just as its inhabitant, a bearded man in his late twenties with rainbow trousers and a coarsely woven orange shirt, emerged to investigate the roars.

They collided. The gun flew from Kelvin's hand to land at the hippy's feet.

The hippy was first to recover. Faced with an armed, deranged, elderly man, he had the presence of mind to grab the gun and take to his heels towards the safety of his fellows. Kelvin was quickly in hot pursuit. Seeing them approach, the crowd parted to receive them into its midst.

The fugitive slipped in the mud of the gateway and Kelvin, adrenalin singing through his bloodstream, was upon him just as Percy pedalled his bicycle the last few yards towards the mob.

Aware that itinerants brought out the beast in his superiors, Constable Percy Green was out and about early as well. He was liable to find his patch engulfed in riot-shielded veterans of the miners' strike if there was any hint of trouble from the hippies.

He had finished his breakfast and donned his bicycle clips by 7.45.

His approach had not gone unnoticed. Many campers, the crowd which had attracted Kelvin had gathered in the gateway, ready to defend themselves against the approaching pig.

'Here! Stop that!' Percy shouted at the two figures who were now rolling on the ground.

He yelled again, but his shout was drowned by a groan of sympathy from the observers as Kelvin kneed his opponent in the balls. As the hippy folded into the foetal position, Kelvin grasped the gun and pulled.

The other's fingers were scrabbling down to protect their greater interests, but a digit must have been caught by the hammers. The click as the gun cocked was immediately followed by an explosion as the cartridge discharged.

Percy, an expression of bemused horror on his face, toppled slowly off his bicycle and disappeared into the ditch.

The sudden pre-Somme silence was broken only by the singing of larks and the grunts of Kelvin. Having regained possession of the smoking gun, he was now using it to belabour his recumbent victim.

'I'll teach you to steal my bloody gun and waste my bloody ammunition!' he panted, standing back to flip the empty cartridge out of the breech and slide in a fresh one.

The itinerants began to wake from their horrified paralysis.

'Christ!' said someone, his voice shaking with terror. 'He's shot the pig! They'll murder us!'

Another, a woman with bare feet and a brown kaftan, was still more afraid of Kelvin. 'Look out! He's loaded the gun again. He's going to shoot someone else!'

'We'd better get the hell out of here!' yelled a shirtless man with the astrological sign for Libra tattooed on his breast.

'Hang on!' shouted a fourth, a man in his fifties with the hair of an Old Testament prophet. 'It would take hours to pack up and we wouldn't get 5 miles! It wasn't our fault, anyway.'

Then the squire and his guest drove by.

The squire had been having a rough time of it. He had expected Candy to lie a-bed until midday before descending the stairs to dally with half a grapefruit and a bottle of vodka. She dallied with the vodka and grapefruit sure enough, but the dallying took place at 7 am. Half an hour later, she would be ready for her day's research. The squire, in his plus fours, had to brave the startled stares of his Charolais cattle as he inspected them at 8 am rather than the accustomed 10.30.

They were now on their way back to the manor for the squire's breakfast.

'Hey!' shouted Candy, as they approached the gateway. 'Isn't that your gardener? Whaddya call him? Yokel! That's it! What's he doing with a gun?'

'I've no idea,' replied the squire, who was looking forward to the kidneys, kippers and kedgeree which he had persuaded Marcia to produce every morning during the visit.

'Well stop! Let's find out!'

'Must we?' asked her host. However, well aware of who was buttering his bread, he was already drawing to a halt.

The man with Libra tattooed on his chest ran over to the squire's estate car. 'He's shot a pig!'

'Kelvin?' queried the squire, winding down the window. 'Shot a pig? Are you sure?'

'Sure I'm sure. He's in the ditch!'

'What an extraordinary thing to do!' The squire frowned. 'You didn't ask him to, did you?'

'No!' cried the Libran, backing away in dismay.

The squire frowned again. 'How very odd! I wonder where the pig came from? There are very few round here.'

'I don't believe this!' blurted Candy.

'It is very strange,' agreed the squire, turning to her. 'Very few people kill and eat their own pigs these days. It's sort of died out. It used to be quite the thing in the old days when every cottage had a sty in the back garden. They used to say that the only bit that couldn't be eaten was the squeal.'

Candy turned a curious colour beneath her tan. 'Oh, you mean a hog kind of pig! I thought you meant a cop!'

The squire gave a snort of laughter. 'This isn't New York, you know. We don't believe in shooting the police in this country!'

'Huh! At least a policeman can defend himself. Shooting an innocent hog is really gross.'

'He hasn't shot a pig . . .' began the Libran.

'Well, why on earth did you say he had?' cried the squire, rounding on his informant. 'Can't you see that you've upset Miss Gutz?'

'Let me finish what I was saying, you old fool.'

'Old fool! Do you know who I am?'

'Don't ask me, mate. I've only just met you. Your passenger might have some idea. Ask her.'

The squire's grandfather gave disrespectful inferiors a taste of his horsewhip but his grandson lacked the same social confidence. He spluttered feebly.

'Anyway, that nutter really has shot a pig. A policeman.'

'A policeman? Don't be absurd!' said the squire.

'He bloody well has!'

'C'mon!' said Candy. 'Yokel must have flipped and he's still got a gun. We're not involved. Let's get out of here.'

'For heaven's sake, shut up, woman!' said the squire. 'I'm going to have to sort this out.'

'Don't you "woman" me! He'll need a getaway car and he might take this and use me as a hostage.'

'Don't be so silly!'

Leaving the car, the squire walked up the lane towards the gateway. The Libran and Candy fell in behind. 'Kelvin! What on earth do you think you're doing?'

Having stopped belabouring his victim, Kelvin was now haranguing the crowd about the evils of trespass. He was thoroughly enjoying himself. Seeing the squire approach, he waved his gun in greeting.

'What are you doing?' repeated the squire.

'Morning, Squire,' replied Kelvin cheerfully. 'I was just about to make a citizen's arrest on this chap,' he indicated the foetally positioned figure at his feet, 'and then do the whole bloody lot of them for trespass!'

The squire examined the prone hippy. 'He's not a policeman, surely? He's rather dirty and can't be 5 feet 8 inches tall.'

'He must have been undercover,' said Candy.

'The pig's in the ditch,' volunteered the Libran. 'That's Les. He's one of us.'

'Is he dead too?' asked the squire.

'I dunno.'

The squire clicked his tongue in exasperation. 'I must say, Kelvin, your behaviour really seems to be disgraceful. These people are not trespassers. They're here by invitation for the village fayre this afternoon.'

'Nobody told me,' said Kelvin sullenly.

'I'm sorry,' said the squire. 'There must have been some breakdown in communications. Even so, it's hardly an excuse to go around shooting them!'

'He's all right.' Kelvin stirred Les with his foot. Curling himself even tighter, the latter squeaked. 'See? Anyway, the bugger pinched my gun!'

'Did he? That's a pretty poor show! I can understand you getting upset.'

'What about the pig?' demanded Candy.

'Oh yes! This chap,' the squire indicated the Libran, 'says that you shot a policeman.'

'Don't know what he's talking about,' growled Kelvin. 'There haven't been any police round here.'

There were noises of dissent from the crowd: 'Go and look in the ditch.'

'That's a good idea,' agreed the squire. 'We'll look in the ditch.'

'Why?' asked Kelvin, puzzled.

'Because that where the dead cop is,' said Candy, keeping safely behind the squire. 'You bastard!'

'Cackling hag!' riposted Kelvin.

The squire cleared his throat. 'Let's sort this out. Where is this late policeman supposed to be?'

'Over here!' called the Libran, keeping at the back of the crowd. It turned in his direction and parted to allow the squire and Kelvin to walk towards the indicated spot.

'Ah!' said the squire in an interested voice, observing the bicycle lying on its side in the rank grass that bordered the tarmac lane. 'That looks like Percy's. Percy! Percy? Are you in the ditch?'

'The pig's dead,' said the Libran.

The pig, invisible beneath the umbellifers of water dropwort that filled the ditch, let out a loud groan.

The Libran turned. 'He's alive! Thank God! Quick! Get the herbalist!'

Kelvin, his gun now both loaded and cocked, walked to the edge of the ditch.

'He's going to finish him off! exclaimed the Libran.

Kelvin stopped and peered through the foliage. 'You're a right dozy bugger, Percy!'

The groans turned to grunts and then to swearing.

'He doesn't sound too badly hurt,' observed the squire.

'He's all right. It same thing happened to him last week.'

'He got shot last week too?' screamed Candy. 'I thought this was the peaceful British countryside. They don't waste pigs like this even in Miami.'

'Don't be stupid!' replied Kelvin with scorn. 'The gun fired into the air. No, if Percy's on his bike and he sees something exciting, he stops and forgets to put his feet down. So he falls off.'

Percy's head was now visible as he struggled to climb out. It was a deep ditch. Kelvin leaned forward to present him with the

barrels of his gun. Percy grabbed hold of them and slowly re-emerged into the morning.

Mud coated his clothes, although his helmet was still perched on the top of his head. He was not a happy policeman. 'I forgot again,' he moaned. 'This uniform was clean on yesterday morning.'

'Are you OK?' asked the Libran.

'I suppose so,' mumbled Percy, walking over to his bicycle to give it a kick. 'Horrible machine,' he added gloomily. 'I suppose that was you shooting, Kelvin?'

'That's right. That's what guns are for and this is a gun, my gun, sure enough.' He patted the stock affectionately.

'Not assaulting anyone with it, were you?'

'Certainly not.'

'Is that right?' asked Percy, turning to the Libran.

The Libran thought for a few seconds before allowing his natural instincts to dominate. 'No, there's not been any trouble.'

'Good! There's not going to be a riot or anything? I'm not going to have to call for reinforcements?'

'Will someone tell me what's going on?' demanded Candy. 'Why can't any of you people talk properly? If I can't understand half of what you say, how the hell can I get my dialogue authentic?'

'This hag here could do with being locked up, Percy, if you want something to do.' Kelvin jerked his thumb at Candy. 'She's a right royal pain in the arse. If it hadn't been for her, there'd have been none of these people here at all. She writes dirty books too.'

'I think we'll forget the whole incident, Kelvin,' said Percy. 'Don't you think that'd be best, Squire?'

'I quite agree. Nobody's been hurt and there's no harm been done, what?'

'I still think that cow should be locked up.'

Candy glared at Kelvin. She may not have understood every word, but there was no mistaking the gist. 'With animals like him around, no wonder this country has gone down the tube.'

Even the squire's eyes went slitty as he escorted her back to the car and the prospect of breakfast.

Given the alternative of slogging their way over the moor, the clouds of most Atlantic depressions preferred to take the easy route up the river valley. Grinding to a halt over Moorcombe, they jettisoned much of their ballast of moisture to climb the forested hillside that rose 1000 feet at the valley's head. So when it rained, it didn't mess about.

During the morning of fayre day the clouds gathered until they were squatting comfortably on the topmost branches of the trees. By lunchtime they were ready to water the village and the surrounding countryside with first drizzle, then downpour and deluge, washing the tourist cigarette packets and sweet wrappers from the streets and ditches into the swelling river.

On Kelvin's field the itinerants must have been used to such conditions. When the heavens opened, they removed sandals and trousers to don black plastic bags and splashed equably about their business, setting out their wares for the afternoon.

The squire had planned a Walter Scott vision of Merrie England, the like of which had never been seen outside a Hollywood sound stage. But it does not rain on sound stages. By the time he jingled into Kelvin's field, his dream had drowned in the rain, the mud and the squalor that was the campers' special contribution.

The jingle came from the harness. In one of the old stables that lay behind the manor, Ivor had found and dusted down a mouldering governess cart. A sour old pony which had bounced children round local gymkhanas for a couple of decades was in the harness.

The squire was not a happy man. Candy was hunched on the seat beside him, enveloped in a long white rubberized mackintosh and black galoshes lent by Marcia. She seemed as miserable as her host. So did the pony which was steaming after dragging the cart the half-mile from the manor.

The field looked like a cross between an eastern bazaar and a WI market. Striped tents sold Afghan sandals and carpets. Khaki tents offered books from *West Coast Lesbian Hotels* to *Zoroastrian Tepee Symbols*. Black tents sold sinister lumps of roughage glued together with toffeed sugar. Grey tents offered pottery looking as if it had been thrown by a slapstick comedian or woollen garments as coarse as a medieval penitent's hair shirt.

Sploshing through the mud was Percy, snuffling optimistically for illegal whiffs of smoke, while the natives grimly offered their usual wares of jam, cakes, white elephants and jumble as islands of tradition amid the alternative sea. The wooden boards of the skittle alley, removed from storage in the shed behind the pub, were overshadowed by a rain-slicked inflatable bladder, waiting for a passing child to scale its slippery flank for a bounce.

Lined up at the entrance to the field to greet the principle guests, the children were otherwise occupied. As the trap squeaked and lurched across the stones placed to reinforce the mud of the gateway, half struck up a depressed rendering of *Nymphs and Shepherds*. The other half wiped the drips off the ends of their noses with their sleeves and shuffled their feet, their song sheets disintegrating in the rain.

'That's awful,' groaned Candy, clutching at the framework of the carriage as its wheels bounced over the rocks.

'I think it's a very good effort,' said the squire, rain trickling off the brim of his deerstalker. 'Blasted animal!'

The squire hauled impotently on the reins, but the pony was

no more inclined than Candy to linger for the serenade. It ambled over to the WI cake stall, ignored the protestations of Mandy who was in charge, and selected a rock cake.

'I think I'd like to go back home,' said Candy.

'Well, you damn well can't!' replied the squire testily. 'A lot of people have gone to a great deal of trouble for this. *Noblesse oblige* and all that.'

'What's that supposed to mean?'

'It means, madam, that one's position in life carries with it certain obligations. If one is to earn the respect of one's tenants and social inferiors, one treats them with courtesy.'

The pony had decided that its teeth were not up to the task of grinding down the rock cake. It spat it into the mud. The gig lurched forward as the animal, taking a bite out of a Victoria sponge, swayed to avoid a blow from Mandy's umbrella.

'Can't you control the thing?' asked Candy.

'I'm doing my best,' said the squire.

In the course of avoiding another swipe from Mandy, the

pony hit a pole supporting the canvas roof of the cake stall. It gave way. The tarpaulin subsided over the stall, discharging the gallon of water that it cradled over the pony's head.

The animal snorted, reared and considered bolting until it recalled the problem of dragging the squire and his companion behind it through the mud. Backing away from the struggling canvas, it contented itself by loosing a mighty fart.

'Damn its eyes!' grunted the squire, sawing at the reins. He looked round for aid.

The commander and Kelvin had emerged from the beer tent a few yards away and were standing comfortably under a golf umbrella from where they could obtain a good view of the proceedings. Having given up their attempts at singing, the nymphs and shepherds had also broken ranks to spectate.

'Commander! Grab this animal's harness!'

'Commander?' queried Candy, following the squire's glance. 'I thought he was supposed to be one of your serfs.'

'Oh, do be quiet!' said the squire. 'Why on earth did I ever get into this charade? Commander, I really could do with some help!'

The commander thought about it for a few seconds before taking hold of the bridle. 'Where do you want me to park it?'

'I don't know. Just hang on to the bloody thing until we get off!'

'Don't you think we'd better give Mandy some help?' asked the commander.

Just emerging from beneath the tarpaulin, Mandy was most unhappy as well as extremely muddy.

'You damn fool!' she shouted at the squire. 'You shouldn't be allowed to be in charge of that beast!'

'The trouble is that he isn't,' said the commander.

'And who's going to pay for these cakes? That bloody horse has ruined them!'

'Huh!' said Candy, clambering down from the conveyance. 'Respect of your social inferiors! That's your maid! There's something phoney going on round here!'

'It's her day off?' suggested the squire. He eased himself down from the driving seat.

'I'm not stupid. No maid would speak to her employer like that!'

'Er . . .' said the squire.

The commander came to the rescue. 'It's been a long-standing tradition in Moorcombe that the housemaid at the manor is free to speak to the squire as she likes.'

'Huh!' snorted Candy. 'If you believe that, you'll believe anything. Where can a girl get a drink round here?'

'We don't let girls drink in this country. They have to be eighteen,' said the commander.

Candy's visage grew even grimmer. 'Let me re-phrase that. Where can a woman get a drink round here?'

The commander remembered his manners. 'Why don't you come over to the beer tent and let me get you something? Squire, take the reins.'

The squire found himself in charge of the pony once more with Mandy bearing down on him.

'Don't leave me! What am I to do with it?'

But he was on his own.

'What would you like to drink?' asked the commander. Since the beer tent was the most congenial place in which to escape the rain, it was crowded with both campers and locals. They found an empty bench and table near the entrance.

'A vodka.'

'Just beer and cider, I'm afraid. You really ought to try the cider. We're famous for it round here.'

'I think you're famous for bullshit. I think I'm being set up. You're supposed to be a gardener, along with that jerk there.'

The jerk muttered an imprecation beneath his breath and waited for Prudence to bring his beer from the bar.

'And I don't know what doohicky town you think I come from,' continued Candy, 'but I'm not swallowing that crap about the maid.'

'Try swallowing the cider instead,' said the commander.

'I might as well.'

'Very wise,' said her companion. Catching Kelvin's eye, he gave him a wink. 'Of course, the maid tradition grew up as a result of an old squire's misuse of *droit de seigneur*.'

'What's that?' demanded Candy.

'It's the custom which allowed the feudal lord to . . . er . . . sample a maiden the night before her marriage.'

'You're kidding!'

'No. It's well documented. Anyway, apparently an ancestor of the present squire kept one of his maids for a week and that was just not on. Isn't that right, Kelvin?'

'What?'

The commander twisted his face in his effort to project his wink.

'Oh! I see,' said Kelvin. 'Sorry. Yes, the maid. Terrible it was. The poor bridegroom was expecting a fortnight's nookie in Blackpool and instead he was kicking his heels outside the manor listening to the cries of his future wife as the squire preyed upon her tender flesh.'

Candy examined Kelvin's face suspiciously. 'Well, at least I understood you that time. But I'm not sure that I believe a word of it.'

'It's true,' insisted Kelvin. 'Squire's *droits* have always been a bit tricky, haven't they, Commander?'

'*Droits*? Oh, yes,' agreed the commander, nodding his head vigorously, 'especially when the squire has been a bit . . . er . . . kinky.'

'Gee! Those days must have been awful. When did that sort of thing die out?'

'Die out?' said the commander. 'Who said anything about them dying out? It takes more than a few socialist governments to change an ancient English custom like that!'

'Come on!' sneered Candy. 'What do you take me for? Nobody would stand for it these days.'

'It's one of our ancient traditions,' argued the commander. 'Look at the beefeater. His uniform hasn't changed since the fifteen-hundreds. It's the same with the *droits*.'

'I'll grant you your beefeater, but not the rape of innocent girls. Not in the late twentieth century.'

'Look!' said Kelvin.

Candy looked. Prudence was coming towards them bearing three pints of beer in her hand. 'So?'

'Look at her belly! That's the squire's.'

Candy looked at the belly.

It was hard for her to miss it as its summit stopped within 8 inches of the end of her nose. Seeing no reason to spend money to clothe a condition that would be over in a few months,

Prudence coped with her bulge by leaving the zip of her jeans undone.

'That was the squire? Dickie?'

'It's the price we sometimes pay to keep our traditions.'

'How awful! The poor thing.'

'It's been a sad business.' Kelvin shook his head to show how sad it had been. 'Prudence here had a thing going with Archie. Archie was born here but went off and got out of our traditional ways. He came back and they got together and she had to go to the squire to give him his *droits*. Archie just didn't understand. So they're not getting married.'

Plonking the drinks on the trestle table, borrowed from the church hall for the occasion, Prudence flopped down on the bench. It sank another 3 inches into the damp soil.

Candy looked up at Prudence, the author in her fired. 'Is this true?'

'Is what true?' asked Prudence, who had no idea what they were talking about.

'That you and Archie aren't getting married,' said Kelvin.

'Yes,' confirmed Prudence.

'It's amazing! But surely the law can do something about it? The squire can surely be taken to court to support the child?' She shook her head. 'No. This is all bullshit! It's got to be bullshit. Not even the British would let this sort of thing go on.'

'What sort of thing?' asked Prudence. 'And why should the squire support the child? It's not his fault. I knew what I was doing.'

'Go and get Candy a cider,' ordered Kelvin.

'All right.' Prudence levered herself obediently to her feet and squelched back to the bar.

'It's not bullshit,' said the commander, thinking of another angle. 'You see the squire's great-grandfather set aside some of the money he'd made in the slave and opium trade and created a trust fund . . .'

'That was the wicked Sir Jaspar!' said Kelvin.

'So it was!' said the commander with delight. 'The lily-white sheets on his bed were legendary.'

'They were that!' confirmed Kelvin.

'Anyway,' continued the commander, 'he created the fund just so that any girl who became pregnant after *droits* would be provided for. It meant that the villagers were very keen to keep the custom going.'

'Why?' asked Candy, looking at Kelvin.

The latter looked hurriedly at the commander.

'Well,' the commander went on, 'well, there aren't too many girls who become pregnant and so there aren't too many calls upon the trust fund. But if one of them gets lucky, she gets about £20,000 a year until the child is twenty-one. It's a jolly good wedding present for a young couple.'

'Good heavens! But what does his wife have to say about it?'

'Whose?'

'Dickie's, the squire's. That lovely Marcia.'

'Oh!' The commander looked to Kelvin for help. It was forthcoming.

'It's nothing to do with her! It's his duty! And every English gentleman has to do his duty, otherwise where would we be?'

'Quite right, Kelvin.' The commander nodded his head vigorously. 'And doing one's duty is not always easy. For example, look at her over there.'

Both Candy and Kelvin followed his instruction. 'Her over there' was one of the itinerants, about 6 feet and 15 stone. She was wearing a badge which stated 'Men are a load of balls'.

'That's Fanny Adams. She was married eighteen months ago and was very cross with the squire when she wasn't pregnant.' The commander shook his head ruefully. 'Not a responsibility I'd fancy.'

'We all know it's not easy for him,' agreed Kelvin. 'Why, I've seen the squire break into a muck sweat when he's been dishing out the prizes at the school sports day and he sees the crop of maids coming up. They say he nearly sold up a few years back when both of the . . . er . . . Loosemire girls got engaged. They were the Ladies West Country Wrestling Champions for five years.'

'Both of them?' asked Candy, quite entranced.

'No,' said the commander, waggling his hand in the air. 'You know. Alternate years.'

'And what happened?' asked Candy.

'He's our squire,' said Kelvin simply. 'He did his duty.'

'My God!' said Candy in tones of great reverence. 'That's amazing!'

118

The commander and Kelvin exchanged a satisfied smirk as Prudence arrived back at the table. She placed a murky glass of cider in front of Candy. The latter looked at her. 'I suppose I'd better congratulate you, dear. Your father's been telling me all about how you got your baby,'

'He has, has he?'

'Yes, and I hope you really get a good settlement. I think the whole thing's astonishing!'

'I'd thank you not to interfere in my affairs,' replied Prudence coolly. 'But I knew what I was doing and I'm not complaining at the financial arrangements.'

'And you really wanted it to happen like this? Aren't you upset that Archie won't marry you.'

'No, it's the baby that I wanted.'

'Wow!' said Candy. 'This is fantastic!'

'I don't see what's so fantastic about it,' said Prudence. 'This sort of thing happens all the time.'

Candy put a thin brown hand on Prudence's arm. 'Take it from me, sweetie, I've been around a bit and it sure doesn't happen all the time. But how could I use it? Who'd believe that something like this could go on? Truth is stranger than fiction.'

'That's very well put,' said the commander. 'But I'm not altogether sure that I agree. Ah! Good! Here's the squire now.'

The squire had come beneath the protective canopy of the tent. Outside, the landscape lay dead under the impact of the rain coming down from the dark grey clouds sitting immovably in the windless sky. The roar of the rain on the canvas tent forced those beneath it to raise their voices to make conversations heard.

The squire shed his coat. Hauling a paisley-patterned cotton handkerchief from the sleeve of the jacket, he wiped the rain from his face. 'It's most unpleasant out there.'

'What have you done with the horse?' asked the commander.

'I tied the brute up outside. Now we're here, ... er ... Candy, I think we'd better do a quick tour round.'

'In these conditions?'

'Remember your research.'

'Research? I've done the best bit sitting right here talking to Prudence! Dickie, you're an old fox. I knew nothing about this. I could have gone away without hearing about how Prudence got pregnant.'

The squire blinked at her. 'Well, yes, I suppose you could. But it didn't occur to me that you'd be interested.'

Candy wagged a finger at him. 'You just wanted to keep it quiet.'

The squire looked uncomprehendingly at Candy and then at Prudence. 'I must admit that it does seem to me the sort of thing that is best kept quiet. I can assure you it did not occur to me that you'd be interested in vulgar tittle-tattle.'

'I most certainly am!'

'And I'm not vulgar tittle-tattle,' added Prudence.

'No, of course you're not, my dear.' The squire patted Prudence on the shoulder. 'I did not mean that. But I'd have thought that ... er ... Candy would be more interested in customs that were peculiar to our country.'

'It strikes me as most peculiar. In fact, it strikes me as downright immoral.'

'Immoral?' repeated the squire. 'If you'll forgive me, . . . er . . . Candy, it surely is rather sweeping to call this sort of thing immoral. Times have changed, after all.'

'That's just the trouble. Times don't seem to have changed round here at all. Don't you feel that you're responsible for this poor child's welfare?' Candy put her arm round Prudence's shoulder.

'I really don't see that it has anything to do with me,' said the squire.

'It doesn't,' agreed Prudence. 'It's just to do with me. I went in with my eyes open.'

'But it's just as much his responsibility!' cried Candy.

The squire sighed, sitting down on the bench beside Kelvin who, with the commander, had been listening spellbound as their red herring leaped over conversational waterfalls and hazards like a spring-running salmon.

'Perhaps all this sort of flummery,' the squire gestured to his soggy plus fours and deerstalker, 'like these clothes and all these servants and things, has given you a slightly old-fashioned vision of the role of a squire in modern society. We don't have real power these days. There are too many bloody bolshies around to let one behave like a country gentleman, taking care of the tenants and things. I'd be delighted to take responsibility for Prudence. I still feel it's my duty to the community. But I can only do what people allow me to do these days and Prudence won't allow me to do anything at all to help. It's very distressing that . . . er . . . Archie won't marry her, of course, but there's plenty of money around.'

Kelvin could not contain his delight. He let out a bellow of glee. 'That's well said, Squire.'

'I think it's disgraceful when the father gets away without any responsibility for his actions,' said Candy frostily. 'You ought to be ashamed of yourself, Dickie!'

'Dammit woman! I can't do anything about it!' shouted the squire. 'I've just explained to you. And will you stop calling me Dickie!'

'It's me that won't marry him, not him that won't marry me,' said Prudence fiercely. 'And my babby's got good blood in him. I chose his father carefully. I knew quite well what I was doing.'

The squire shrugged at Candy. 'See what I mean? She's very independent, as Kelvin will confirm.'

'Your behaviour's disgusting!' snapped Candy.

The squire dithered for a moment, assessing the strength of the various emotions that were sloshing about inside him. Candy was paying for her keep but, on the other hand, being told that he was disgusting on such a slim pretext really was a bit stiff. Yes, much too stiff.

He drew himself frostily erect. 'Madam, you are a foreigner and a guest in my house . . .'

'I'm paying,' snapped Candy. 'I'm not stupid, you know. It was obvious some sort of flim-flam was going on with all that *Tom Jones* shit and your stupid clothes, but I thought it was just to impress me. But you were obviously trying to conceal the depth of the moral turpitude of this community.'

'Decadent,' said Kelvin happily. 'That's what we are, aren't we, Commander? And we don't think there's anything wrong with the way the squire has treated Prudence at all.'

'Quite right,' agreed the commander.

'In fact, the squire's a real old-fashioned English gentleman. He treats every woman the same. He wouldn't treat you any different from the way he's treated Prudence.' Kelvin leered into Candy's startled eyes. 'It's your duty, isn't it, Squire? All those generations before you who've been at the manor and been a father to the tenants. You couldn't let down the family tradition. You don't mind what they look like or what age they are, do you?'

'No, of course not.'

'And you're due to go away again in just a couple of days, I believe, Miss Gutz. That leaves only a couple of nights.'

'That's quite enough!' snapped Candy, rising to her feet. 'I've had it. I'm not staying in this place a moment longer.'

'Do you want to go back to the manor now?' asked the squire hopefully. 'It should be time for tea when we get back.'

'I want someone to run me to the station. I want to go back to London now! I wouldn't share a house or even an automobile with you for a million bucks. You're disgusting! Just you wait until my book comes out! I'll make you an object of opprobrium all over the world!'

She swept imperiously towards the rain, pausing just before

she left the protection of the canvas. 'Come on, then, you two. You're taking me!'

Kelvin and the commander drained their pints and buttoned up the top collars of their coats.

Kelvin winked at the squire. 'This ought to be worth a tip! She has paid in advance for the stay, I suppose?'

'Yes,' said the squire. 'But I don't understand what's going on.'

'I wouldn't worry about it as long as we're rid of her.' He and the commander followed Candy into the rain.

The squire sighed. 'What was all that about, Prudence?'

'Dunno. Funny woman, I thought.'

'Yes. American, you know. She didn't even say thank you.' He sat down on the bench. 'I suppose I'd better let Ivor know that everyone can go home now.'

'That'd be nice.'

'I wonder what "opprobrium" means?'

'Dunno.'

Chapter Seven

Open Day

'I WENT to a conference yesterday,' said Ivor.

Kelvin yawned, his top plate falling from his gums. Shutting his mouth, he smacked his lips a few times.

The commander frowned. 'I do wish you would put your hand over your mouth when you yawn, Kelvin.'

'There's no reason why your teeth have to be so badly fitting,' said Lindy. 'If you went to the dentist, you could get a decent set.'

Kelvin smiled. 'It's all right. These suit me.' Leaning forward in his chair, he took a decorous sip from his glass. He smacked his lips again. 'This is the life!'

Moorcombe was enjoying an Indian summer. A day or two earlier Stephanie had taken a table and a couple of chairs out into the garden behind the Hunted Hind. After pouring scorn

and derision on those who drank in beer gardens, Kelvin had picked up a chair and followed her example.

Now they all did. Until the midges came out in the evening, they sat on the lawn passing comment on the six red Devon steers in the field beyond the barbed wire fence. This annoyed Bill since they belonged to him.

'One of the topics was public access to farm land,' continued Ivor.

'Load of crap, if you ask me,' growled Kelvin. 'The public's just ignorant.'

Ivor nodded vigorously. 'Certainly that point of view was expressed, Kelvin. Public ignorance about agriculture is one of the greatest problems.'

'Well, it may be your problem, but it's not going to be mine. Shoot the buggers, that's what I always say.'

'I've decided that I'm going to do something about it,' said Ivor.

'Do something about what?'

'About public ignorance. So I'm going to have an open day.' Ivor looked modestly round his peers for their reaction.

'What the hell's an open day?' asked Kelvin.

'You invite the public to come and look round your farm. You show them milking and let the children stroke the calves and clamber all over the tractors – that sort of thing.'

Kelvin grunted. 'You need your head read. You can't go around encouraging them. Shove a shotgun in their bellies. Then they don't come back.'

Ivor sighed. 'Anyway, I'm going to organize an open day on the farm. The Ministry of Agriculture is helping, and I'm hoping people round about will act as guides and explain what is going on to the public.'

'You mean us?' asked the commander.

'Yes.'

'When would it be?' asked Kelvin.

'They thought that a Sunday would be best. There's nothing happening round here on a Sunday and the tourists would probably come along just for something to do. They're the people we want to educate. Every tourist who goes back to the city and says farmers are wonderful is vitally important. At least, that's what they said at the conference.'

'How much would you pay if I decided to help?' asked Kelvin.

'Nothing,' replied Ivor patiently. 'I won't even be charging visitors for parking or admission.'

'It'll need a hell of a lot of organization,' said the commander. 'Lavatories and things like that don't grow on trees.'

'You could make money on a tea and bun stall,' suggested Kelvin. 'Prudence would do it. She hasn't got much work on a Sunday and her belly wouldn't get in the way.'

'That's not a bad idea,' said Ivor. 'I'll suggest it to the Ministry chap. Can I count on some help?'

'If I've nothing better to do I might come along,' said Kelvin grudgingly.

'Oh good. You too, Commander?'

The commander almost purred. He loved to be considered a proper farmer rather than just another pensioner of the MoD or the Colonial Office. 'Gosh, yes. Thanks. I'd be delighted. Although I have to admit I don't know a great deal about dairy farming.'

'It won't matter. You can stand by the parlour door and tell people where the toilets are.'

On the morning of Open Day, well before 11 am, the commander had taken up his station on the steps of Ivor's dairy.

He knew his duties. Cars were to be parked in the field opposite. Since it was used by the milk lorry to turn each morning after sucking out Ivor's tank, the gateway was wide enough for the most trepid holiday driver. The commander also knew the location of lavatories.

Rocking on his heels, he clasped his hands behind his back, drawing in the morning air. From his position a yard above the level of the lane, he could see above the hedgerows. Across the fields, some still blurred by mist, others studded with black-and-white cows or dotted with sheep, was the square tower of the church above the trees and the thatched roof of the Hunted Hind. Far beyond, the bulk of Dartmoor was faintly etched against the sky.

An hour later, Kelvin arrived in his Land Rover with Bill.

The commander frowned as they drew up beside him. 'You're late.'

'You're bloody lucky we're here at all,' replied Kelvin. 'What are you doing standing in the middle of the road?'

'I'm in charge of parking.'

'Well, open the gate and let us in.'

'Everyone's got to park in that field,' replied the commander, indicating the opposite gateway.

'Don't be silly. We're staff. We can park in the farm yard.'

'I'm sorry, but you have to go in the field with everyone else.'

Grumbling, Kelvin crashed into gear and ground his way into the field. The commander reassumed his station in the middle of the lane, waiting to direct the next vehicle.

Kelvin and Bill re-appeared.

'Where's all the other cars, then?' asked Kelvin.

The entrance to the farm yard lay to the right of the dairy. Kelvin looked over the gates across the snowy concrete, but there were no cars parked by the cubicle sheds or the hay barn. Lifting its head above the rails of its pen by the gate, Ivor's massive Friesian bull showed the whites of its eyes and snorted.

'There aren't any others yet. You're the first.'

'Is that a visitor, Commander?' Ivor's voice came from inside the dairy.

'Is what a visitor?' asked the commander, looking carefully up and down the lane in case someone was slipping along the hedgerow.

Ivor appeared in the doorway at the top of the steps. His face fell when he saw Kelvin and Bill. 'Oh, I thought I heard a car.'

'It must have been me,' replied Kelvin. 'Since nobody's coming, can we go home?'

Ivor sighed. 'It's extremely galling. We've gone to a great deal of effort to tidy everything up and the cubicle shed is full of advisers with displays and things. Now this happens.'

'Can we go, then?' repeated Kelvin. 'I was thinking we could go to the pub. You could come along too.'

'We can't pack up just yet. The head Ministry chap forgot to place any adverts but the local radio station's putting it out now. So I'll have to hang around for a bit. I'd be grateful if you both would as well. I put a few cans of beer in a tractor cab in the stack yard for you.'

'Sshh!' The commander held up his hand, his head cocked to

one side. They all listened. 'It's a car engine! Coming down the lane!'

'He's right!' exclaimed Ivor. 'Commander, take up your position. We'll hide in the dairy. If it's a visitor, we'll run through and tell everyone else.'

The other three scurried up the stairs to the dairy. Ivor pulled the steel door almost shut behind him, leaving a crack through which to see what was going on.

Holding up his arm, the commander stepped to the side of the lane as the car, a small blue saloon, pulled up beside him.

'Good morning,' he said to the driver, a man in his seventies with a flat cap and thick spectacles. 'Would you park the car in the field through on the right? There's plenty of room.'

The driver peered suspiciously up at the commander. 'What's going on here?'

'It's an open day.'

'What's 'e say, dear?' asked his passenger. Obviously his wife, she was wrapped in a thick red coat with a map spread on her knees.

'Dunno. He's not making sense.'

The pair must have been hard of hearing as their voices were plainly audible inside the dairy, echoing off the huge steel milk tank and the bare concrete walls and floor. 'Damn!' whispered Ivor. 'I was hoping he'd have heard it on the radio. He's just a passer-by.'

The wife nudged her husband in the ribs. 'Tell him to get out of the way. I don't much like the look of him. He's got a very silly moustache.'

Kelvin laughed.

Ivor frowned. 'Be quiet, Kelvin. They'll hear us.'

'So what? I can't think why we're hiding here anyway.'

'If we were all out there, we'd frighten them off.' Turning back to the crack, Ivor's foot struck the steel door, pealing it like theatrical thunder.

'What was that?' cried the wife.

'Expansion,' replied the commander crisply. 'See? The sun's just touched the dairy door. Now if you'd park in the field, you can be shown round the farm.'

'Shown round? It's Open Day on a farm, is it?' asked the driver.

'Yes.'

'He wants us to look round a farm, dear.'

'I want my lunch!'

'Mildred wants her lunch,' said the driver. 'Perhaps we'll come back after.'

'It's a bit early for lunch, isn't it?'

'He says it's a bit early for lunch, dear.'

'But we're on holiday, Stanley.'

'We're on holiday,' said the driver.

Bending down, the commander leered through the window at Mildred. 'You can have lunch inside, madam. We've got a refreshment stall.'

'What's 'e say?'

'They've got refreshments, dear.'

'What sort of refreshments?'

'What sort of refreshments?'

'What sort of refreshments does your wife want?'

'What sort of refreshments do you want, dear?'

'I want a proper sit-down meal.'

'She wants . . .'

'Yes, I heard,' interrupted the commander. 'She can sit in the barn. We've set out lots of hay bales. Then after lunch you can have splendid fun. Your wife can see the . . . er . . . calfies being fed and the chickens and the ducklings and . . . er . . . things like that. Kittens, yes, kittens too.'

'They can do a sit-down meal, dear.'

'A bit of roast pork? Can they do a nice bit of roast pork?'

'Yes,' said the commander, beginning to lose patience. 'Farm fresh. Select your own pig and it's slaughtered and cooked before your very eyes and you can still look round the farm afterwards.'

'He says there's roast pork, dear.'

'Is the pork safe?'

'Yes, dear. It's like that fish in Spain last winter.'

'What fish?'

'The ones that were in the aquarium in the restaurant. He says we choose our own pig.'

'Oh, that's all right then. It should be nice and fresh.' Mildred leaned across to speak directly to the commander.

'You have to be so careful with pork in this hot weather, I always think. Don't you agree?'

'Shall I park the car then, dear?'

'Yes.'

The commander waved the car through into the field and hurried over to the dairy door. 'I've got you a couple, Ivor.'

'I heard. But what the hell were you talking about? Kill your own pig! There's something extremely sinister about the idea.'

'I do agree. However, you needed visitors and I've got some. I can show them where the loo is as well.'

'Bugger the loo! What am I supposed to do about this pork lunch? I've got a litter of eight-week-old pigs, but I'm not going to chop a bit off one for her.'

'I'll do it,' said Kelvin.

'You bloody well won't! It's one of the most macabre ideas I've ever heard.'

'No, I'd show them a pig and then get a takeaway from the café. They do roast pork on Sundays.'

'Well, it's entirely up to you. I think the whole thing is absurd. Today has all the hallmarks of being a disaster.'

Muttering to himself, Ivor went through the dairy into the milking parlour.

Kelvin chuckled. 'How much do you think I can charge for a plate of roast pork, Bill?'

'How much does it cost at the café?'

'£4.95. But that's if you eat it there. I should think he'd sell me a takeaway for . . . I dunno . . . three quid, perhaps?'

'You might get away with a tenner, then. You could make quite a production of the farm-fresh bit.'

'Ten quid!' said Kelvin happily. 'That's worth having. And here's another car! They'll be wanting feeding too. I must just go and have a word with the commander. I'll put him on commission.'

The Great British Public eventually flowed into the car park. Not in floods or in trickles, but in spurts.

After the elderly couple, a ten-minute hiatus ensued before the results of the radio exhortations began to dribble through. The commander herded them into small groups which set out on tours of the farm under the guidance of local farmers or Ministry advisers.

Having been busy at the start of the day ferrying food from the café, Kelvin was relishing the prospect of a bit of action when he approached the commander's corral. 'Afternoon, Commander. What have you got for me?'

'I've got a nice little group ready.' The visitors were milling uneasily beside the milking parlour under the baleful eye of the bull. The commander clapped his hands to get their attention. 'Good afternoon. This gentleman is a farmer, Mr Morchard. He is going to show you round and answer your questions.'

They looked suspiciously at Kelvin. In response to a slap from his mother a small boy, who had been trying to scale the fence to Ivor's slurry pit, began to wail. Kelvin fixed the child with a glare, shutting him up.

'Right,' he said, 'I'm here to eddicate you lot on what a farm is all about. How many of you think you know something about agriculture already?'

Tentative murmurs came from the group.

Kelvin put up a restraining hand. 'Not all at once! If any of you have a question or a comment, please raise your hand. Yes you!' He indicated a middle-aged man in a powder-blue cashmere sweater with the name of a nearby golf club embroidered on the left breast.

'I know a bit about farming.'

'You do, do you? And how's that?'

'Through my job. Some of my clients are farmers.'

'Oh? What's your job?'

He gave a self-deprecating smile. 'I'm a bank manager,' he said, earning respectful looks from the rest of the group.

'A bank manager! A bloody money salesman! I've never met one of you lot who's known anything about anything.' Kelvin snorted his contempt. 'Of all the salesmen that plague the farmer, bank managers are the most ignorant of the lot! And you think yourselves so bloody important! I don't have much respect for money lenders.'

The commander was still close by. He cleared his throat nervously as the unfortunate visitor wilted under the onslaught. 'You must admit, Kelvin, that it's very good of Mr . . . er . . . to come along this afternoon to learn something.'

'I suppose so,' admitted Kelvin grudgingly.

'And I'm sure you will be extremely helpful to him – and polite.'

'Will I?'

'Yes,' said the commander firmly, 'and to everyone else.' Then he continued, lowering his voice, 'Who knows? Make it interesting enough and they might tip you.'

After pausing for a few seconds' thought, Kelvin turned back to his group, displaying the full horror of his smile for their benefit. The child burst into wails once more. 'That's right, sonny. You'd do well not to climb over the fence. That's 10 feet of shit there. Go through and you'd be swallowed up.'

Mother grabbed hold of child and the others gazed at the pit with added interest.

'You wouldn't think it, would you?' continued Kelvin, winking at the commander as he realized he had got their attention. 'A friend of mine cleared a slurry pit a couple of years ago and found the skeletons of five cows at the bottom. The farmer had thought they'd been stolen.'

'That's terrible!' exclaimed one of the group, a girl in her early twenties with open-toed sandals. She had her arm wound round the waist of a willowy youth.

Kelvin smiled. 'I knew another farmer whose brakes failed on his tractor and in he went.' He paused to allow time for their imaginations to appreciate the situation. When they had all shuddered, he continued. 'Fortunately, he'd just put on one of those new-fangled sound-proof cabs which are virtually air-tight.'

'Christ! He was lucky,' said the bank manager. 'How long was he there for?'

Kelvin shook his head. 'It can't have been very nice for him. It was an hour before they realized he was missing and another half-hour after that before they got the tractor out.'

There was a nervous titter from a young man with greasy hair and a black biker's jacket. 'Cor! Think on that! That long trapped in the dark and the slurry. I think I'd go mad.'

'Yes,' agreed the bank manager. 'What did he say when they got him out?'

'Not a lot,' replied Kelvin. 'You can't really say much with a mouthful of shit. They reckoned it took fifteen minutes before the cab filled and he choked to death.'

There was a retching noise from a fat woman with bleached hair.

'How was that?' muttered Kelvin to the commander. 'Do you think that's the sort of thing that'll keep their interest?'

'You may have overdone it a bit there,' replied the commander after a critical look at the audience. 'Is it true?'

'It might be, for all I know,' said Kelvin.

'Mum! I like farms,' lisped the child.

'Quiet, dear. That was a very sad story.' She held up her hand. 'Excuse me, but do you think that it could happen in this slurry pit?'

Kelvin considered the commander's assessment of the situation and dismissed it, secure in his own understanding of human nature.

'It was this very slurry pit!'

Cries were wrenched from almost every lip and the lovers clutched each other with a desperation that did not owe everything to lust.

133

'Kelvin, for heaven's sake . . .' The commander was silenced by the sight of hands waving above the group.

'You!' said Kelvin, pointing at the fat woman with bleached hair.

'Can we go through the fence for a closer look?'

Kelvin shot the commander a triumphant glance. 'Certainly not! The ground turns to quicksand just inside the fence and you'd slide inex . . . inextricorably . . .'

'Inexorably,' murmured the commander.

'. . . Inexorably into the pit and we could do nothing but watch.'

'You could throw her a rope and we could pull,' suggested the biker.

'We'd rip her in half,' said Kelvin.

The bank manager frowned. 'I don't quite see why.'

'I told you you didn't know anything about farming,' said Kelvin. 'The suction from cow slurry is terrific. It has to be. If it weren't for the suction, it would be spraying out the back end of the cow the whole time, particularly when she's feeding on spring grass. Now, if you'll all come this way, I'll show you the shed where a farmhand was once killed by the bull . . .'

'Are you doing all right, Commander?' Ivor had just waved off a group in the direction of the car park.

'Yes, fine. I've been keeping tally and we've had sixty-eight people through including these.' The commander indicated a motley bunch of urbanites standing patiently by the dairy.

'I hope they're better than my last lot. Four of them were Young Farmers. One of them said very rude things about the docks in some of my fields.'

'You should be all right, I think,' replied the commander. 'Do you see the man with the two boys?'

'Yes.'

'He's already said he's always wanted to know how you train the cows to stand still over the milk bottles.'

'Oh good! That's much more the sort of thing that I was expecting.'

'He's also of the opinion that you shouldn't be allowed to keep a dangerous animal like your bull so close to the road. And that farmers are overpaid spongers.'

'Does he now?' Ivor sighed. He was finding the day a bit of a strain. 'Well, I suppose that's the sort of public that we wanted to get here to educate.'

Introducing himself, he led his new group in the direction of the stack yards. He drew them up by the machinery. The group examined the tractors and equipment in respectful silence.

'What's that for?' asked the man with the two children. He was down to one child. The other had run up to the nearest tractor and was tugging at the door of the cab. Ivor had locked it and removed the key.

'That is a mower-conditioner with an 8-foot cut,' said Ivor.

'For cutting what?' asked the man. He had white shoes, a gold bracelet and a gold chain which disappeared inside his red shirt.

'Grass,' replied Ivor.

'Really? It looks very expensive for something that just cuts grass. And what do you do with the clippings?' Ivor mutely indicated the bales, piled high in the Dutch barn opposite. The man walked over and poked a bale. 'This is hay, surely?'

Ivor nodded.

'Hay's a crop,' said the man accusingly.

'That's right,' confirmed Ivor. 'I'm not sure I get the drift of your point.'

'I wanted to know what you did with the grass clippings. They must make an awful mess of the fields.'

'Hay is made from grass.'

'Oh.' The expert was rather taken aback, particularly as he heard a giggle from his remaining son and his wife, but he counter-attacked, pointing at another machine. 'What's that thing for?' He peered at the metal plate attached. 'It's foreign, German. Bloody farmers! They should buy British and keep our own workers in jobs.'

Smiling doggedly, Ivor moved on towards the barn containing the calf pens. This was more successful. The group stood and drooled.

'Oh, aren't they sweet!' said the expert's wife.

Ivor cleared his throat. 'The predominant enterprise here is dairy farming. You will see the cows later. The lactation of a cow is 305 days, after which she is dried off and then has her calf and the process begins again. In a sense the calves are a by-product of the process and, except for those that are reared as replacements for the herd, they are sold in the market. We try to improve the quality of the herd by careful selection of the bulls . . .'

'What's wrong with that one?' interrupted the expert, indicating one of the dozen calves inside the pen.

Ivor looked at it. 'I don't think there's anything wrong with it.'

'Yes, there is. It's different from the others and it's got something dangling from its belly. It's deformed.'

'Poor little sod,' said a woman with a face as hard as a hatchet.

'I think you'll find that it's different because its father was a Hereford bull instead of a Friesian like all the others. Its mother was a heifer – that's an animal that has not had a calf before – and Hereford calves tend to be smaller and make for easier calvings which is why we use a Hereford bull on heifers. The white face is very distinctive.'

'What about the dangly bit?'

'The remains of the umbilical cord.'

The calves had been having rather a good day. Four bales of lovely clean straw had been scattered across the dung on the floor of their pen. In addition, people kept leaning over the wall of their pen billing and cooing at them, breaking the monotony of their short lives. They crowded up the wall to sniff and nuzzle at the extended hands.

Amid the cries of saccharine delight, the expert struck a single discordant note. 'They're starving! Look at the way they're sucking our fingers!'

'Can we feed them?' implored his wife to a chorus of agreement.

'It's not quite as easy as that,' said Ivor. 'Most of these were removed from their mothers only a day or two ago and aren't properly trained to the bucket. Anyway, they were fed this morning.

'Huh!' sneered the expert. 'You should have the RSPCA put on to you. Any fool can give a baby animal milk and you can't tell me the little deformed one had any breakfast.'

Ivor gritted his teeth. He was beginning to feel some hostility towards this particular member of the Great British Public. 'I can assure you that it is in my own interests to keep the calves healthy and happy in order that I might receive the best possible price for them in the market.'

'*Ut*,' said an elderly man with grey hair and a hairy wart on his nose, opening his mouth for the first time.

'I beg your pardon?' asked Ivor.

'*Ut*. That was a fine example of a consecutive clause, "in order that". In Latin that would be "*ut*" plus the subjunctive. I used to teach classics.'

'How fascinating,' said Ivor.

'Sodding nutter,' muttered the expert.

'Ah! Sodding: perhaps a colloquial use of the gerund?'

'These here calves are maltreated,' continued the expert heavily. 'They're obviously starving.'

'Right!' said Ivor, briskly. 'I shall go and get some milk and you can show us all how it's done.'

This suggestion met with unalloyed approval from the group and a smirk of triumph from the expert. Ivor trotted back to the dairy to return with a bucket containing a couple of pints of milk. He handed it to the expert. 'Right,' he repeated, opening the gate into the calf pen. 'In you go and let's see you feed the Hereford.'

The expert took the bucket. 'Here!' he said, laying his hand on the yellow plastic. 'This milk isn't fresh. It's warm.'

'I can assure you that it was fresh from the cow this very morning. However hard you try to train them, it doesn't come out of the animal already refrigerated.'

'Don't you take that tone with me!' responded the expert, picking up the edge of irony.

'I'm sorry that you find it offensive.'

Glaring at Ivor, the expert brushed past him into the pen. Ivor was pleased to hear the dung under the straw squelch beneath his white leather shoes. The expert ploughed his way through the frisking calves towards the Hereford which backed into a corner. He placed the bucket in front of it. 'There you are, calf. A bit of food at last!'

The calf made a break for it, knocking over the bucket as it went.

'You have to hold on to the bucket,' said Ivor more

cheerfully. 'I thought that might happen so, fortunately, I brought along another.'

The expert grabbed the bucket over the wall. 'I don't need any advice from you.' He approached the calf once more. It dashed for the security of its fellows, but the expert hooked an arm round its neck to prevent its escape. A grunt of respect from Ivor was drowned by the dismay of the female members of the group.

'Don't hurt it! Poor little thing.'

Breathing a touch more heavily than he had been, the expert did not deign to answer, but straddled the calf, holding it in place with his knees. Keeping a tight hold on the rim, he grounded the bucket in front of its nose.

The calf, as calves do, bawled.

Ivor began to enjoy himself still more. 'Look at it from the calf's point of view,' he suggested, settling his elbows comfortably on to a wad of sacking lying on top of the wall. 'In its limited experience, milk is something that needs to be sucked from a sort of stalagmite . . .'

'Stalactite,' corrected the Latin scholar.

'Thank you . . . stalactite that hangs from its mother's belly. It doesn't even know what milk looks like because it's never seen it. So clamping it between your knees in front of a plastic bucket containing a mysterious white liquid, and expecting it to know what to do about it, is asking rather more of the creature than it is capable of.'

'Consider also,' intoned the scholar, 'that the animal does not yet know how to eat or how to drink. All its nutritional needs are fulfilled through the agency of sucking at this stalactite.'

'Thank you,' smiled Ivor.

'My pleasure,' responded the scholar gravely.

'Okay, so you think you know better,' said the expert, his ear an inch from the source of the bawl.

'Although I'm a farmer and have been doing it for twenty-five years,' said Ivor, 'I'm sure you know just as well as I do. I'm sure you learned the trick of dipping your fingers in the milk, letting the calf suck and then slowly leading its head down towards the bucket just as long ago as I did.'

'I'm sure he did,' agreed the scholar.

'Course I know what to do,' said the expert.

'I know, I know,' nodded Ivor, looking vaguely round at the straw bales stacked across the shed. 'When you've fed the calf, we'll go and watch the cows being milked. They should be coming into the parlour soon.'

The expert dipped his fingers fastidiously in the milk and waved them in front of the calf's nose. It bawled.

Another dip. This time there was an edge of roughness in the way that he stuffed his fingers into the calf's mouth. It sucked for a second before removing its head to bawl.

Sensing progress, the expert repeated the exercise and lured the calf's head an inch towards the bucket.

His wife clapped her hands. 'Well done, it knows about the milk now!'

The expert risked a sneering smile at Ivor.

'Well done!' agreed Ivor charitably. Collecting two bales, he arranged them into a seat. He beckoned to the scholar and they sat down.

In another couple of minutes, the calf's nose actually touched the milk. But there were problems in other areas. Never before having been under restraint, the animal had bought its battery of defenses into action. These included kicking and struggling, together with some wriggling and writhing. Slowly its captor sank to his knees as he fought for control.

Bringing other weapons into play, the calf rubbed its teeth against the expert's fingers, gradually stripping the skin from the back of the first phalanges of his index and medius. Mother Nature had also given it the ability to take as much liquid in its nasal orifices as would not have disgraced a small elephant. Consequently, when it raised its head from the bucket to bawl, it sprayed the expert with lukewarm milk.

In spite of admonitions from his wife, supported by many of the group less able to appreciate the stress that he was under, the expert put his hand firmly behind the calf's head and held it into the bucket, giving the animal the age-old choice of drink or drown. The calf was forced to employ its ultimate weapon.

It is little known that the most noxious substance known to mankind is the shit of a young calf. In spite of not being banned or even mentioned in the Geneva Convention, only one belligerent has ever dared use it as a weapon of war for fear of the terrible retaliation. Like nerve gas it was stockpiled by both sides in the Second World War, but its sole recorded use was by the Japanese in Manchuria in 1940. The crack Yamato-takeru battery experimented with it in the assault on Anyang, but the premature detonation of a shit-shell resulted in mass suicide of the entire unit.

Extruding a buttercup-yellow turd against the expert's red shirt front, the calf waggled its abdomen, mashing it well into the material. Uttering a low groan of horror, the expert staggered back against the pen wall.

Kelvin's group, meanwhile, had been enjoying their tour. They had thrilled to the shock of an electric fence. They had watched Kelvin tease the bull into snorting rage. They had been told how to add sugar to fertilizer in order to make a bomb. Their visit to the calf pens promised to be an anticlimax.

'Ah!' said Kelvin, taking in the scene as he led them through the door. 'This might be worth watching!' He smiled a greeting to Ivor. 'Trying to bucket-feed a calf, is he?'

Ivor nodded. 'That's right. It's just er . . .'

'Has it, by God?' He turned to his group. 'Quickly! Line up against the wall beside the others, but I'd advise you all to breathe through your mouths.'

His followers had learned to put faith in their leader. Led by the bank manager, they pushed their way through Ivor's group to the wall of the pen just as, with a cry of despairing rage, the expert flung himself back upon the calf. Achieving a stylish step-over leg lock, he thrust its head into the milk. At the same time, he sank his teeth into the calf's ear.

''Tis a terrible thing,' said Kelvin, shaking his head, 'what an unco-operative beast can do to the human spirit.'

'True,' agreed Ivor.

The calf surfaced above the milk. It bawled and bawled again. It had bawled before, but this time the results were more dramatic. The herd was coming in to be milked.

Mooching gently towards the collecting yard were a hundred cows, including the ex-heifer whose offspring was being abused. At the first bawl, the herd stopped, pricked up its ears and swung its head towards the cubicle shed beyond which lay the calves. At the second bawl, the ex-heifer replied, breaking into a trot towards the sound. The pangs of deprived motherhood were not far beneath the surface of the rest of the herd either and they followed.

His attention caught by the terrible splintering sound as the door at the far end of the cubicle shed was ripped off its hinges, Kelvin hurriedly ushered his group into a vacant calf pen. In a burst of charity, he allowed Ivor's group to join them. He was only just in time.

Across the yard from the calf pens, the other door of the shed fell like a drawbridge with a mighty crash and the cows spilled into view.

'Good Lord!' cried the scholar, scurrying further up the heap of bales.

Ivor was rather braver. He stood in the passage like Horatius with only an empty bucket as, led by the ex-heifer, the herd thundered across the yard towards him.

'Jump!' yelled Kelvin, as the calf bawled once more. Ivor jumped out of the way, swinging his legs neatly into the pen beside the others.

The ex-heifer, still in the lead, was into the swing of wrenching aside Ivor's doors. Few could have stood up to the impact of 800 lb travelling at 15 mph. The bolt securing the calf pen exploded out of the concrete-block wall and the deprived mother was there, sliding across the floor of the pen.

For a second, the spectators could appreciate the frozen tableau – the expert holding the calf in a step-over leg lock, his face a mask of terror – before a wave of slurry-based straw rose in front of the ex-heifer to bury it. Coming to a halt, she glowered down at the twitching heap of straw.

'Marvellous!' exclaimed the bank manager from the safety of the adjacent pen. 'Will he be trampled to death?'

'It's possible,' said the scholar. He was 8 feet up the stack of bales on the other side of the passage from the calf pens with half a dozen milling cows between himself and the others. 'There are occasional cases of people being killed by cows, usually in just these circumstances when a mother is trying to protect her calf.'

'It's very rare, though,' said Ivor. 'We'd better try and sort this lot out, Kelvin.'

The straw in the calf pen heaved as the calf staggered to its feet. It trotted over to its mother, its tail waggling, and buried its head into her udder. The cows milled and mooed outside in the passage as the other calves wondered through the broken door to join them.

The straw twitched as the expert slowly rose to his feet, his face ashen. His white shoes were mostly brown. His red shirt was stuck to his torso by a yellow smear of shit. His grey slacks had damp patches on the knees and another darker damp patch spreading from his crotch.

'Oh, dear,' said Kelvin, shaking his head sadly.

'Well done!' called Ivor. 'It may not be the usual way, but, by God, you've certainly got some milk into that calf!'

Chapter Eight

Gold

THE LATCH clicked, the hinges creaked and Kelvin, ducking his head expertly beneath the stone lintel, strutted into the pub. From the semi-circle of high stools round the bar, the other patrons examined him suspiciously. He appeared to be in a good mood.

Bill looked at him with a jaundiced eye. 'Had a good day, Kelvin?'

'I'll say I did. D'you know Ralph Ridd over beyond Larks Common, Bill?'

'Course I do. It's a very sad business. The poor bugger was selling half his cows in the market today to pay for his kid's medical fees in America.'

'That's the one! I took a bit of milk out of the best of the cows before she went into the ring so that she looked light in her back left quarter.' He rubbed his hands together in glee. 'I got her for £200 less than she's worth! Who's going to buy me a drink to celebrate?'

Nobody appeared to be diving into their wallets to demonstrate their delight at his good fortune. Kelvin's smile vanished and was replaced by a frown.

'Have you managed to have a word with Archie yet?' asked the commander spitefully.

'Mind your own business!' replied Kelvin, perching himself on a stool and slapping the top of the oak bar with his hand. 'I'm not going to have my troubles talked about. D'y'understand?'

'Oh yes,' replied the commander, delighted that he had managed to draw storm clouds across the sunshine of Kelvin's day.

'Good!' Kelvin nodded his head fiercely. 'I can't understand it. He's been down here twice in the last month and each time I've only heard about it from Prudence after he's been gone. I don't understand her these days.'

'Do you think you ever understood her?' asked the commander delicately.

'Understood her?' Kelvin wrinkled his brow. 'I don't suppose I did really. There was never any need to.' He paused to think about the question. 'I had better things to do than try to understand her. She was never any trouble, see? She always did what she was told.'

'You'll never get anywhere if you treat people like that,' said Annie sagely from her bench by the window.

'I know that now, Annie,' said Kelvin, swivelling on his stool to look at her. 'I remember when she used to go and play sometimes with an old sack she pretended was a doll when she should have been working.' He shook his head sadly. 'That was where I went wrong. I was too soft on her. If I'd beaten her more often when she did it, then she might not be defying me now.'

'Defying you, is she?' Bill squinted sideways at Kelvin through the smoke from his cigarette. 'I'm surprised at you, Kelvin, letting her defy you.'

Plastic squeaked as Kelvin ground his teeth. 'Don't you see? There's nothing I can do to stop her! I can't say I'll cut her pocket money 'cos she never gets any. I can't say I'll make her work harder 'cos she does all the milking and everything already. And I can't hit her 'cos I never hit a woman.'

'Not a pregnant woman, anyway,' said Bill.

'No, not when she's so obviously carrying like Prudence is now. She's must have seen Archie several times behind my back in the last months, but she says it's none of my business when I ask her about the financial arrangements they're making and I can't think of anything I can do about it.'

'Well, it isn't your business is it?' said the commander. The pub growled its agreement, but Kelvin was too wrapped up in his own distress to notice.

'She's going to have the brat in a few weeks and, as far as I know, she's not arranged for anyone to take over her work.'

Stretching across the bar, he poured himself a beer. 'She's turned selfish too. I told her that the best place for the baby to sleep would be the barn and she said she'd move out before that happened! Move out!'

'Come off it, Kelvin,' scoffed Mandy, 'you can't honestly expect her to keep the baby in a barn!'

'I don't see why not. If it was good enough for Jesus, it ought to be good enough for Brett.'

'Face it, Kelvin,' said Jimmy, 'you're going to have to put up with the kid if you're going to keep Prudence.'

'But I don't want a bloody kid bawling and shitting all over the house!' wailed Kelvin. 'At my age I want a bit of peace! The least that bugger Spontini should be doing is paying me compensation. It's not fair!'

'It's a real shame,' said the commander soothingly. 'However, I did hear that Archie was going to be down this weekend. He asked me to meet him in one of his fields tomorrow because he's thinking of putting in a boating lake and wants my advice. You could pop over and see him.'

Kelvin perked up. 'Really? Coo! If I go round tomorrow I ought to be able to catch him and sort things out. Thank Christ for that! What time are you going there? And why on earth does he want to ask you for advice?'

'Eleven in the morning, and he knows I'm a naval man and thought I would know something about the water. I can talk to him about anchorages and the possibility of dangerous winds. That sort of thing.'

Kelvin shook his head as if to check on a headache. 'A boating lake! I don't know whether he's dafter for thinking of it or for asking you about it. Anchorages, indeed!'

The commander tightened his lips beneath his moustache. 'Look, Kelvin, I'm trying to help you. I'm not interested in listening to your opinions.'

Kelvin pulled his horns in grudgingly. 'All right, keep your hair on. I'm grateful to you. I'll surprise him. Whereabouts are you going to be?'

'Down on the river meadow where he wants the lake.'

'What? The field that runs opposite mine by the river? He can't tear it up! It's the best on the farm! I was going to grow barley there when I got that field off him. I'm going to have a few words with Archie Spontini! For Christ's sake, someone buy me another drink!'

The Spontini acres kissed the ancestral plot of the Morchards at several points: across the lane, through a wood and along the river. Kelvin waited until 11.15 when Prudence and her growing bulge were safely ensconced in the yard, paring the feet of some cows.

Putting on his gumboots, he scurried out of the back door, down the unkempt garden path past the outside privy and on towards his flat field and the river. He peered cautiously round the trunk of a venerable oak that had survived since his chainsaw had broken down a couple of years earlier. On the other side of the river, he was gratified to see the commander and Archie in earnest conversation.

Kelvin splashed across the river under cover of a willow which sagged half-way across from Spontini's side. By crouching below the bank, he was able to get within 20 yards of the others before erupting from shelter. He covered the final distance in a few swift strides.

'Morning,' he said, stepping between Archie and the route towards the field gate.

His greeting had a deleterious effect upon the equanimity of both men. The commander jumped while Archie lurched violently on his shooting stick, grabbing at the commander's arm to prevent himself falling to the ground.

'Aaagh!' shrieked Archie. 'Don't let him do it, Commander! Protect me!'

Some had been heard to say words to the effect that Kelvin was a peculiarly unpleasant man. An elderly undertaker, retired to the area on the strength of a *Down Your Way* programme from a neighbouring village, would ostentatiously leave the pub whenever Kelvin entered. But only his cattle dog normally greeted him in quite such a craven fashion.

He stopped, baffled. 'What's wrong with you?'

'Oh, don't. Please don't,' pleaded Archie.

Shifting uneasily from boot to boot, Kelvin looked at the commander. 'Do you know what this is about?'

'You did give us both quite a fright.'

Kelvin scratched the back of his neck. 'Well, yes. Perhaps I

did.' He waved his other hand at Archie. 'But not as much as
that.'

The commander looked at Archie. 'No, I see what you
mean.' He carefully unpicked Archie's pudgie hand from the
sleeve of his jacket. 'It's all right, old chap. Kelvin's not going to
hurt you.'

Archie peered round the commander at Kelvin. His spaniel
eyes were shaded by the brim of a tweed cap festooned with
multi-coloured fishing flies. 'He's not? But Prudence said that
you were going to kill me! She said you were going to stick me
with a pitchfork. She said you were furious.'

'Did she now?' said Kelvin thoughtfully. 'Well, you can see
you're going to be all right for the moment.' He spread his arms.
'You see? No pitchfork anywhere.'

'But . . . but . . . Prudence said . . .' Archie's babble trailed
into silence.

'I don't know what little game Prudence is playing,' said
Kelvin, 'but she's obviously up to something.' He tried a
winning smile. 'I don't want to kill you. I just want to make sure
that you're aware of your responsibilities. This here idea of
a lake, for instance. It's not on, you know.' In response to
the winning smile, Archie had sneaked back behind the

commander. 'Look! Will you please stop hiding! You're making me embarrassed.'

Archie crept out from behind his shelter. 'You aren't angry with me?'

'Angry? Well, of course I was a bit unhappy. You debauched my Prudence, after all.' Archie slithered back behind the commander. 'I'm not angry now, though!' continued Kelvin angrily. 'I was a bit peeved, I must admit. What with you being a foreigner and not wanting to marry her and save her from her shame. But I'm now concerned that you make proper provision for the little bastard.'

Archie emerged into full daylight. 'But I want to marry her!' he cried.

'What? But she says you have . . . what was it, Commander?'

'A beautiful relationship,' supplied the latter.

'Yes. That's what she said.'

'Yes, we have got a beautiful relationship,' quavered Archie, 'but I want more!' He was wearing a camelhair coat which made him look like a large teddy bear. 'I've known women before, lots of women. But I've never known anyone like Prudence. She's bewitching! She's wonderful! She'd make the perfect helpmeet for me in my new life in the country. And I love her. I want her to marry me, but she won't!'

There was a dumbfounded silence.

'Well, bugger me!' said Kelvin. 'That there speech takes some thinking about!'

'Doesn't it?' agreed the commander. 'A most moving declaration. Tell me, though, Archie. Might I ask in what way Prudence is bewitching? She's awfully nice and all that, but bewitching?' He looked down at Archie with as much curiosity as a gentleman might properly display after being driven to ask a question of such impertinence.

'Yeah,' said Kelvin. 'She's a good worker and cheap to keep, but I've never thought of her as bewitching.'

Archie looked at them. 'It's her sweetness, intelligence, beauty and innocence, I suppose.'

Frowning as he strove to understand, Kelvin scratched his head. 'I can understand the innocence bit. Apart from her Uncle Charlie, I don't think she's known another man.'

'It's her sexuality too,' continued Archie dreamily. 'It just oozes out of her, don't you agree, Commander?'

'Er . . .' said the commander as he and Kelvin exchanged baffled glances.

'I suppose it could be something to do with the tight sweaters she's taken to wearing,' said Kelvin.

'Must be, I suppose,' agreed the commander. 'Bit odd, though.'

'Yeah.' Kelvin cleared his throat awkwardly. 'What I really wanted to talk about, Archie, was the cost of this here business. Quite apart from the baby, there's the cost to me. Prudence is working at the moment but a baby is bound to make it more difficult for her and I can't look after it when she's milking 'cos I'd be in the pub. I'll need compensation.'

'I've offered Prudence money but she refuses it.'

'Get on with you!' exclaimed Kelvin with scorn. 'You didn't offer her a damn thing. She's my daughter and wouldn't turn down money!'

'She did,' insisted Archie. 'She said there was a whole trunk full of her old baby clothes in the attic which Brett could wear and that food was free from the farm. She didn't want anything from me.'

Kelvin squared his shoulders. 'She must have gone potty,' he announced bluntly. 'And it's up to us to make sure we act in the best interests of her and the child, whatever she wants. Don't you agree?'

'Oh yes,' said the commander, responding to an encouraging glare.

Archie was less sure. 'That's all very well, but if she won't take anything from me, I don't see what can be done.'

'Course we can do something. F'rinstance you can set up a trust fund. I'll look after the money and administer it in the interests of Prudence and the child. You're going to acknowledge Brett as your heir, of course?'

'Well, I hadn't really thought about it.'

'About bloody time you did, then. He's your only descendent? You haven't got any other little bastards kicking about, have you?'

'Er . . . not that I know of.'

'Then you ought to start thinking seriously about your tax

position. If you died this afternoon . . .' Archie automatically moved in the direction of the commander but halted in response to an imperious wave from Kelvin. 'If you kicked the bucket this afternoon, the tax man would take half the farm. But if you handed it over to Brett and kept going for a bit, he wouldn't have to pay any tax at all.' Kelvin eyed Archie critically. 'You look as if you should be good for a few more years.'

'I'm not sure I understand,' said Archie. 'Are you saying I give this farm to a trust you intend to set up for Brett? In effect, I hand the farm over to you?'

'That's right. At least I'm a farmer and this place would be run properly.' Kelvin's eyes took on a manic gleam as his brain imagined the future. 'Brett'll inherit from me – eventually. I would amalgamate the farms and run them as one enterprise. I'd sell off your house and invest in improvements to my buildings. Think of it!'

Archie turned to the commander with a nervous giggle. 'Commander, he's joking isn't he?'

The commander spread his hands. 'This is nothing to do with me, for heaven's sake! I'm not involved at all.'

'But you're an interested spectator,' said Kelvin with rare irony.

'True,' acknowledged the commander contentedly. On a pleasant morning, with the river chuckling past, he had nothing better to do. Moreover, he was witnessing an important scene in an important subplot in the fascinating soap opera of life.

Opening time at the pub, however, was beginning to loom.

Archie found a point to pursue. 'Kelvin, you're a bit older than me, right?'

'I'll be sixty-two next birthday, but I still do a full day's work.'

'I don't doubt it,' said Archie hurriedly. 'But the point I'm making is that I'm fifteen years younger than you. If the problem is surviving for the next seven years to avoid tax, wouldn't it be better to make me the trustee for your farm, rather than the other way round?'

Kelvin chuckled. 'Don't be silly, Archie. That'd be quite different.'

'Okay,' agreed Archie. 'I suppose that's a bit too much for

you to understand.' He thought for a moment or two. 'How about this? Prudence is younger than both of us. If you gave Southcott to Prudence in trust for Brett, I might consider doing the same with Middlecott.'

Kelvin's chuckle died. He gasped. 'Give Southcott to Prudence? What sort of a man do you think I am? I've farmed that place ever since my father died when I was seventeen years old. I'm not going to give it away at my age. Especially not to a woman. And especially not to Prudence. Not now she's shown she's no better than she should be!'

'Do you think I could let you and Kelvin get on with your negotiations without me?' asked the commander. 'I don't think there's much else I can tell you about the lake. The only problem I can foresee is the chance of unpredictable fluctuations in winds due to the gaps in the woods.'

'You're not going to leave me alone with Kelvin!' exclaimed Archie.

''Fraid so. It's most interesting, but you really have to sort everything out between yourselves.'

'But what's the rush?'

'The pub.' Elaboration was unnecessary.

'I'll see you there later, then, Commander,' said Kelvin. 'after Archie and I have sorted this business out.'

'Oh dear,' said Archie gloomily. 'I supposed you'd better come to the house for a cup of tea.'

'That's civil of you, but I'd prefer a whisky.'

Putting his arm tenderly round Archie's shoulders, Kelvin led him across the field. At the gate, the commander turned right and the other two turned left.

The commander had news. Arriving in the pub twenty minutes after opening, he took his barley wine and sat waiting for the undivided attention of the patrons. Negotiations had started between Archie and Kelvin.

'It's not been much of a summer so far,' Mick was saying gloomily. He was in his thirties, a burly man with short black hair and bushy brows. His main source of income was the café which he ran with his wife Beryl. He was also chief of the fire brigade, which quenched conflagrations all over the moor.

'Oh, I wouldn't say that,' replied Bill. 'A couple of nice dry spells let us get in the silage and there's been plenty of rain to keep things growing nicely.'

'All this pissing drizzle may be all right for the grass, but it's no damn good for tourists. Beryl was saying her ice cream takings are down 23 per cent. We needed another summer like '76.'

'Or '55 and '47,' added Ivor.

' '47 was a winter,' said Bill. 'You mean '40. I'll never forget the summer of 1940. Cloudless blue skies and the best cider apple crop I ever saw.'

'Battle of Britain too,' said Ivor.

'Was it? That would have been upcountry, though.'

' '89. That was the hottest of the lot,' said Jimmy.

' '89? We haven't had '89 yet,' said Bill scornfully.

'I meant 1889,' said Jimmy with a triumphant smile.

'Silly old fool,' muttered Mick. He rapped his glass on the bar to regain the floor. 'The economy of Moorcombe isn't just farming any more. It's tourism too, and if there's bad weather in the season we all suffer: us in the café, the pub, the garage, the post office and all the shops. Even the church collection is down this year.'

'You ought to extend the season,' said the commander. 'By the way, Archie . . .'

Mick turned savagely towards him. 'If it was that easy, we'd have done it years ago. You need an attraction. We've only got hills and heather and views. We need a good cave or a beach or something like that, then they'd come any time.'

'Incidentally,' said the commander, seizing his opportunity, 'Archie and Kelvin have had a meeting.'

'What?' demanded Bill, swinging round to stare at him. 'They've actually met?'

'Yes. I was there.'

'Well, why didn't you say so?'

'I didn't have a chance.'

Outside the pub a car engine roared, an engine under great stress.

'Who the hell's that?' said Jimmy with a frown.

'Dunno,' said Bill, also frowning. There was a crunch. 'He ain't got any headlights now, anyway.'

A car door slammed and the door to the pub crashed open. Kelvin filled the frame.

'Gold!' he bellowed, staggering towards the bar. 'Gold!' Grabbing Malcolm's whisky from the oak counter, he tossed it down. 'Gold!'

The commander cleared his throat. 'It sounds as if your little chat with Archie went all right.'

'Here!' shouted Malcolm, recovering from his shock. 'That was my drink! What do you think you're doing?'

Kelvin clutched Malcolm's arm, red blotches visible on his cheeks beneath the grey stubble. 'Gold!'

'Gold,' agreed Bill. 'Will you stop burbling and tell us what all the excitement's about?'

'Archie. He's discovered gold in the river. Gold!'

'Gold?' Bill curled his lip. 'Get a hold of yourself, man. There isn't any gold round here.'

'Look!'

Rummaging in his pocket, he pulled out a polythene coin bag. 'He lent me this.' He emptied its contents on to a beer mat on the counter. It appeared to be grit. 'Gold!'

The pub peered at it. 'That's just grit,' said Bill.

'It's gold! Look at it! It glitters and Archie knows his gold. He was in Australia for a bit, he said.'

The pub peered at it once more.

'It does glitter a little,' admitted Bill.

'And there's certainly gold in the Welsh hills,' said Malcolm. 'They always go and dig a bit out when one of the royals needs a wedding ring.'

'There's gold almost everywhere. The only trouble is, it's rarely possible to extract it at a profit,' added the commander, stirring the grit with a dubious finger.

'I can't say I've ever heard of any round here,' said Jimmy, shaking his head.

'All the same, I suppose there's bound to be. There'll be alluvial gold in the river, washed down from the granite of the moor.'

'That's right!' exclaimed Kelvin. 'He had a sort of tin dish. He said you slosh the gravel around and the heavier bits of gold sink to the bottom of the pan while the lighter stuff washes away.'

The pub had gone quiet as the patrons listened.

'The bottom of the river's all stony, though,' said Bill. 'I don't see how he can pan boulders.'

'There's a bit of gravel on the edge of his field going into the river and that's where he got it from. See that little pile of grit?' He had no need to draw their attention to it. 'In that little pile, there's 4 ounces! It's heavy stuff, gold. Archie must be mad. He gave me this gold and he doesn't even know how much there is! I could take a bit and he'd never notice!'

Lindy clicked her tongue in disapproval. 'He's the father of your grandchild, Kelvin. You shouldn't be trying to rip him off.'

'I'm not!' said Kelvin emphatically. 'I told him it was very trusting of him and he just laughed. "There's plenty more where it came from," he said. Can you imagine it? Bloody gold! Piles of the stuff! He said he'd let me take some as compensation for Brett!'

Jimmy spat contemptuously. 'That bugger! He comes down here with piles of money and as soon as he gets here he finds piles more!'

'This is ridiculous!' said Lindy. 'It can't be gold. The best it can be is that – what d'you call it? – fool's gold.'

'Iron pyrites,' said the commander knowingly. 'I must say, it seems highly unlikely gold's been at the bottom of that river since the Stone Age and nobody ever spotted it until Archie Spontini came along.'

'I don't see why,' objected Mick. 'If he had a gold mine in Australia, he's probably the first bloke who could tell. Archie must know the real thing from the fake and I'll take his word for it because it certainly looks like gold to me.'

'You'd be a fool!' said Lindy.

'If you see a fiver lying on the ground, you don't walk past just in case it's a forgery. You grab it and check it out later.' He heaved himself to his feet. 'Anyway, I must be off. I've got a busy afternoon ahead. We've got a fire to put out. Can't waste time in idle chatter.'

'Oh, well, take care.'

The pub stopped looking at the gold to nod farewell as he went through the door.

Jimmy leaned forward and blew softly on the pile of grit. 'It's gold right enough. Not a grain of it moved.'

'Course it's gold!' said Kelvin. He frowned. 'Here! How come Mick knew he had a fire this afternoon? I mean, the whole point of a fire is you don't know it's going to happen.'

'That's true!' agreed the commander. 'Perhaps it's some-body burning straw and wants the fire brigade to stand by.'

'We don't burn straw round here,' said Kelvin. 'We use it for feed or bedding.'

'All right, it was just a suggestion. Perhaps there's another reason.'

Clutching at the counter, Kelvin uttered a hoarse cry. 'Aargh! The bugger's going after the gold by himself!' Grab-bing the beer mat, he hurriedly poured the gold into his handkerchief. 'I'm not having that! I'll see you lot around!'

'I'm coming too!' said the pub.

Kelvin led a scrum of patrons through the door and, for the first time in the recorded history of the Hunted Hind, drinks were left unfinished in the public bar.

Having strewn broken glass from his headlights across the entrance to the car park, Kelvin had a head start on the others. He roared back to his farm to collect a shovel and a large dish used originally for making clotted cream. He donned his gumboots, stuffed an empty jam jar into his pocket and scuttled down the garden towards the river.

He arrived on the bank, his lungs fighting to obtain oxygen through the tar of half a century's heavy smoking. Nobody else was in sight.

Having already been shown where the seam of gravel lay, he splashed across the river and wasted no time in plunging his shovel beneath the water. Bending over, he scooped up some of the gravel. With great care, he lifted the shovel from the water, emptying it into his dish. He grasped the dish in both hands and swirled it in the manner that he had observed in the cinema. The gravel gathered itself protectively in the centre of the dish.

Kelvin frowned. Something else was meant to take place. Somehow the gravel and water was supposed to separate from the gold. He gave the dish a more vigorous swirl and half its

contents slopped over the edge and down his trousers to trickle into his gumboots.

'Bugger it!'

He tried again. This time there was a scattering of glitter in the centre of the bowl. Kelvin grunted in satisfaction, returning to his gravel with a whistle.

The barking of a dog broke his absorbed concentration. Lifting his head, he saw most of the regular patrons of the pub hurrying across the field towards the river. He had been expecting it but, nevertheless, he scowled ferociously.

Placing the dish on the bank, he waded a few yards downstream to where a willow leaned over the river. He ripped three straight wands from it, returned to the seam of gravel and drove the sticks into the bed of the river.

Mick was first to the bank, carrying a bucket and a garden trowel. He was panting. 'Have you found anything · yet, Kelvin?'

'None of your business,' replied Kelvin sourly.

Mick hesitated for a couple of seconds before stepping down into the river, splashing over towards the gravel.

'What do you think you're doing?' shouted Kelvin.

'What?' Mick was startled at his aggression. 'I'm going to pan for gold like you.'

'Well, you can't.'

'I bloody well can,' objected Mick. 'I've got as much right to be here as you.'

'I've staked a claim,' said Kelvin, indicating the willow wands poking incongruously above the water. 'All the gold here is mine now.'

The bank of the river was filling up with panting men.

'What's going on?' demanded Ivor.

'Kelvin says he's staked a claim to this bit,' replied Mick.

'Damn right I have! And this is the only gravelly bit too. You won't find anything anywhere else!'

'Staked a claim, have you?' said Bill. 'Right! We'll soon sort that one out!'

Bill was in the river and had the willow wands floating downstream before Kelvin could do anything about it.

'Here!' shouted Kelvin indignantly. 'What do you think you're doing? You're breaking the law. I have a legal claim.'

'You're not in the Yukon in the nineteenth century,' replied Ivor. 'All mineral rights belong to the Crown, so bugger off!' He jumped into the river.

'Bastards!' said Kelvin as the others began to delve into the gravel. 'I was perfectly happy until you lot turned up! None of you have any right to go on the river banks. I've got permission from Archie. You lot haven't and I'm certainly not going to let you over on my side.'

'You're a miserable, selfish, old git!' shouted Mick. 'The river's not private property.'

'The land on either side is and I've got permission to dig into Archie's bank to follow the seam. You haven't.'

The commander raised a pacifying arm. 'Wait! Kelvin, did he really say you could dig into that bank?'

'Yes,' said Kelvin shortly.

'Well, why don't we get organized and do the job properly? If we all agreed to share what we find, we could have some people on picks and shovels and some panning and we'd all do well. It would stop us squabbling too.'

'Here!' yelled Kelvin. 'This is my patch and mine alone. It's me that's got the permission.'

'If you don't shut up, Kelvin, I'll chuck you in the river,' replied the commander.

'Oh yeah?' said Kelvin, hefting his shovel. 'You and whose army?'

'I think everyone else will fight under my command,' said the commander, looking round at his eager neighbours, 'so pull yourself together. If we co-operate, we'll all get rich.'

'Bloody communist,' muttered Kelvin. 'You've been listening to that wife of yours again.'

'Elfrieda is not a communist. And I would thank you to keep a civil tongue in your head.'

'I've got an idea,' said Jimmy before the red-faced Kelvin could respond. 'Why don't we get a ditch digger. Then we could strip away the top soil and get to the gravel more easily.'

Jimmy had hobbled across the field to watch, but his arthritis prevented him from joining in the search.

'It would be a bit drastic,' said Ivor. 'Archie wouldn't like it if we made a mess. Nor would the Water Board.'

'It would be Archie's own fault,' said Kelvin eagerly. 'He gave me permission, remember – permission to dig into the bank. He's going to London to try and flog his nursing homes again, so he wouldn't be able to stop us until he got back.'

'We could borrow a generator and run a pressure washer off it. It would hose out the lighter stuff and leave the gold behind. They do that sort of thing on the clay down in Cornwall. We'd make millions!' said Jimmy.

Bill looked up at Jimmy approvingly. 'You're thinking well today.'

Kelvin paddled over. He was beginning to see the possibilities. 'I'll let you come across my field with your tractor and digger, Ivor.'

Leaning on his shovel, Ivor blinked doubtfully. 'We're going to look damn silly if it turns out not to be gold.'

'I don't think we've much to worry about,' said Malcolm. 'Look at the evidence. One, we all saw the bag Kelvin brought into the pub. Two, it contained a heavy yellow glittery metal. Three, Archie, who says he knows his gold, says it is gold. There seems to be no reason why he should say it was if it wasn't, and it certainly looked like gold to me . . .'

' . . . And to Kelvin,' added Bill. 'Remember you used to have lots of sovereigns which your grandfather collected in a milk churn? You must know gold too.'

'That's right. I know gold when I see it,' Kelvin confirmed.

'Exactly!' said Malcolm. 'So the probability is that it is gold.'

Climbing out of the river to stand by Jimmy, Bill swished idly at a thistle with his bucket, sending a blizzard of down into the air. It drifted on the wind across the field towards the hedge behind which rose the wooded hillside. 'I don't get what Archie's game is, all the same. If you've found a goldmine, you don't rush around telling everybody about it.'

'Ah! But you do! Kelvin did, didn't he?' said Jimmy. 'They're always tottering into the bar in cowboy films saying there's gold in them thar hills. You'd think they'd want to keep it secret, but they never do. You were almost exactly true to life, Kelvin. 'Cept the gold was in the river, of course.'

'That's perfectly true.' Bill squared his shoulders as he shed his burden of doubt.

The commander shivered. 'Look. Why don't we go home and have tea? Ivor can get his tractor and we can all come back later today and sort this business out properly.'

'Who'd have thought it?' said Bill as they walked back towards the lane. He shook his head and laughed. 'A bloody goldstrike in the river!'

Three hours of daylight still remained when the gate into the field on Kelvin's side of the river opened and Ivor's new tractor roared through. The resident rabbits stopped chewing their diet of rushes to stare in awe at the unaccustomed sight of a tractor with shiny paintwork. To them, tractors had always been slurry-brown, spraying oil and shedding flakes of rust. This tractor, however, was big and blue and beautiful, with the yellow arm and cab of the ditch digger attached to its back. A packed Land Rover followed behind. The tractor bounced across the fields and came to a halt about 70 yards from the river.

Drawing up alongside, Kelvin climbed out of the passenger door of the Land Rover and looked up at Ivor inside his sound-proofed, padded, quadrophonic, wrap-round-vision, velour-carpeted cab. He opened the door. 'What's wrong?'

'There's people at the river,' said Ivor, switching off his engine.

'Oh.' Kelvin returned to his own door with an anxious frown. 'There's people at the river. You don't think that's why Archie was so easy about things? He'd probably already told the authorities about the gold.'

'Let's have a look,' said the commander, who was driving. He led an exodus from the Land Rover, passengers clambering up on top of its bonnet or taking commanding positions upon the tractor. Kelvin shaded his eyes against the low evening sun.

'There!'

Both the commander and Bill shouted at once. A head had popped up over the bank and disappeared again.

'How very odd. I can't think what they're playing at,' said Ivor. 'Has anyone any idea what we do now?' He sounded disappointed. 'I suppose we've lost our chance. Damn it! We ought to have struck while we had the opportunity.'

'Well, I'm not giving up that easily,' said Kelvin. 'It's my field up to the river and I've every right to go there. I'm not scared of some government lackey.'

They all piled back into the vehicle, Ivor clattering after them. His machine, unbalanced by the weight of the digger, swayed across the humps and tussocks, unrolling its footprint across the patches of sog. It rocked to a halt by the Land Rover on the river bank.

'I must say, I was not expecting picnickers,' said the commander, looking through the windscreen.

'They're Hell's Angels!' said Kelvin. 'Bloody cheek! They've got no right to be here. Go on, Commander. You go chase them off! There are only four of them.'

Although without motor cycles, the picnickers were in traditional attire: studded leather waistcoats, bushy hair and beards, pot bellies and tattoos.

The commander dismissed Kelvin's suggestion. 'I think we ought to wait till they've gone.'

'Ivor, you go and shift them,' said Kelvin. 'The commander's chicken.'

Ivor looked down at the four and considered. 'No. I think you

161

should go. It's your land they might trespass on and it was you that used to be a special constable.'

'Well put,' agreed the commander, while murmurs of agreement came from Bill and Malcolm in the back beside him.

'Perhaps the commander's right,' said Kelvin, staring through the windscreen at the interlopers. 'Perhaps we should wait until they've gone. I mean, it's not going to be much of a picnic for them with us staring at them. You could rev up the engine and make it noisy as well.'

The four Hell's Angels were sitting on the far side of the river chewing chicken limbs. One, with a coal-scuttle helmet on his head, scowled and shook a drumstick. Another, with long, lank black hair contained by a head band, rose to his feet, tossing the beer can that he had been holding into the river.

'Heavens!' murmured the commander. 'He's a giant!'

'He's not even 6 feet tall,' said Kelvin uneasily.

'Nor's a gorilla!'

'His eyebrows meet in the middle,' said Malcolm with some awe as the Angel stared across the river with beetling brows. 'I think he's looking at me.'

The Angel, in calf-length leather boots, lumbered into the water, wading over towards their bank. He paused by the edge of the river, his way forward blocked by a tree trunk washed down by a flood the previous winter.

'He's just a barrel of lard,' said Kelvin, but the tentative note in his voice was echoed in the sigh of the commander as the Angel casually lifted aside the tree. He topped the bank like a Sherman tank and paused, rocking slightly on his heels, as he searched for a target. He selected the Land Rover and squelched towards it. Both Kelvin and the commander clicked their respective door locks.

Hesitating in front of the bonnet, the Angel walked round to the passenger side – Kelvin's side. Kelvin gripped the door handle.

The Angel stopped outside the window. Kelvin's voice was a panicky whisper. 'Drive away, Commander. Quick! Before he chucks us in the river.'

'Let's find out what he wants,' said the commander.

'For Christ's sake, drive away!' Kelvin essayed a friendly smile through the windscreen.

The Angel brought up a hand, huge, oil-stained, calloused, with a heavy signet ring on the little finger. He tapped it against the window. 'What's he doing?' muttered Kelvin, a glassy grin spreading across his face. 'What shall I do?'

'Open the window. He wants to talk,' advised the commander.

Kelvin slithered along the bench, keeping a firm hold on the door handle as the Angel peered through the glass, darkening the interior as his leather-clad black bulk blocked out the light. He grabbed hold of the handle and shook it. The vehicle rocked on its springs.

'Ohmygod!' gabbled Kelvin.

The leather in the Angel's jacket sleeve bulged. The mechanism of the lock clunked as a piece of metal succumbed to the load. The door was wrenched open and the mighty stench of feral humanity blew in through the gap. 'Orright?'

'He's ripped it off,' said Kelvin faintly.

'He's like something from *Star Trek*,' said the commander.

'Eh?' The Angel blinked his eyes in puzzlement. He flapped his fist at the door. It soughed through the air like the wrecking ball of a crane. 'Your door. It must have been broke. I mended it for you.'

'I've got a black belt in karate,' said Kelvin.

'What's that?' The Angel frowned. Under the strain of the circumstances, Kelvin's false teeth had slipped, making his speech even less intelligible than usual.

The commander put a restraining hand on Kelvin's shoulder, not that he needed much restraining. 'I think he's friendly.'

Kelvin gulped. 'How the hell do you know?'

'I had all sorts of people under my command. You learn how to judge a man at sea.'

'I bet you didn't have many like him.'

The Angel frowned up at Ivor. 'Nice day, isn't it?'

'Is it? Yes, I suppose it is.' Feeling protected by the size of the tractor, Ivor risked a wisp of aggression. 'You're on private property, you know.'

'Eh?' The frown deepened.

'But it's not mine!' added Ivor hastily. 'It belongs to him.' He nodded at Kelvin.

163

The Angel's black eyes returned to Kelvin. The latter gulped. 'I don't normally allow trespassers,' he said. 'In fact, I never allow trespassers . . . er . . . normally. But the river's not private. And the field opposite belongs to Archie Spontini and he's gone to London.'

'Is the gold yours, then?'

'Aah!'

The cry was torn from Kelvin's soul. He slid along the seat and out of the Land Rover, chattering his teeth in agitation. The Angel stepped back from the door but Kelvin thrust out his arm, grasping him by the lapel of his jacket. 'Who told you about the gold?'

The Angel blinked. 'I'm sorry. Have I said something to upset you?'

'Answer me! Where did you hear about the gold, you big jessie!'

'We haven't done anything wrong.' Putting his hands on either side of Kelvin's chest, the Angel lifted him gently and effortlessly on to the bonnet of the Land Rover.

Malcolm chuckled. 'It looks like Kelvin's opened his big mouth once too often.'

'Get your hands off me!' spluttered Kelvin, his face reddening. 'I'll have you know I used to be a special constable.'

'Careful! They don't like the police!' called Ivor.

Spirits had lifted remarkably once it was clear that Kelvin was the focus of the Angel's attention.

The Angel turned from Kelvin. 'Look. We don't need no hassle. A little fat bald bloke was telling us about it down at the garage back there . . .'

'That's Archie!' exclaimed the commander. 'What's he think he's doing?'

'We thought we'd come along and see what was up. We need a bit of bread.'

Sliding down from his perch, Kelvin eased his jacket from his armpits. 'Are you looking for a job?'

The Angel rubbed his hands across the front of his T-shirt. Kelvin recoiled as an armpit gaped, releasing a complex mix of powerful odours. 'Well . . . yes. If you put it like that, I suppose we are.'

'What can you do?'

'My mate Henry was a tin miner in Cornwall once.'

'Really? And how about you?'

'I'm Rupert. I used to be an immigration officer at Heathrow.'

Kelvin snorted. 'And what about the other two?'

'They're our old ladies.'

'What? They're women?!' Kelvin strode to the bank of the river and stared across.

The Angel on the other side waved his chicken limb.

Kelvin returned. 'You're right. They could be women. You poor bastard!'

Blinking, the Angel scratched his belly. 'Yeah, well. It stands to reason, really. I mean unless she fancies a bit of rough, your average skirt has got to be a bit desperate to be a biker.'

'I know what you mean. You stink like billy goat.'

'Do I?' The Angel seemed slightly flattered. 'Well, so do they.'

'You don't surprise me. Do they do anything?'

'Not a lot. Dawn used to be a beautician. They can both cook a bit but it's pretty horrible. We're on holiday, you see, and getting a bit low on cash.'

'If you want cash, you've come to the wrong place. But what we can do is offer you a percentage of what we find.'

'How much?'

'One per cent.'

'That's not much.'

'Look, mate, it's not a piece of one of your friend's tin mines we're offering. If we find enough, you'd be millionaires. Gold, you dope, gold!'

'We're looking for somewhere to crash.'

'What?'

'To sleep.'

'If you put in a good few hours now, I'll let you use my hay barn tonight.'

'You've got a deal.' Rupert swallowed Kelvin's substantial mitt in his own.

Kelvin patted it. 'Now you run back across the river and tell your little friends they're working for me and we'll get the tractor and digger over.'

'Right.' Rupert turned his back on the Land Rover and lumbered into the river.

The day was dying before Jimmy had another idea. An outcrop of rock jutted from the river a couple of hundred yards downstream of the gravel bed. It ran for 40 feet, just above water level, virtually flat save for a half a dozen crevices cutting across it. By damming the river, its flow could be directed across the rock. Gravel shovelled into the flow would be washed down while the heavier gold would become caught in the crevices.

The panners greeted the plan with enthusiasm, turning in their shovels and assortment of crockery. It was agreed that the operation should begin again in the morning.

By 11.30 am the following day, the work was well under way. Ivor had dammed the river with his digger and a powerful chute of water was running smoothly over the rock. The gravel was barrowed across the field to the edge of the bank, where it was dumped into the flow. Stationed in the water, Kelvin and the commander used rubber-bladed slurry scrapers to start the gravel on its way downstream. Gold was emerging from the river at the rate of a matchboxful per barrowland.

Further upstream the Angels were still panning. Both bikes had been brought across the field and a couple of loudspeakers had been dug out of their saddlebags. These were connected to the battery of one of the motorcycles and were filling the morning with loud rock music, attracting a crowd of scruffy beeves on Kelvin's side of the river.

'Did Prudence and Archie sort things out, Kelvin?' asked the commander, leaning on the handle of his scraper as he watched the water scour away the hump of gravel that had just been deposited.

'To tell you the truth, I clean forgot to ask. This business drove it right out of my head. She was at the top of the farm replacing a gate post after milking this morning and I didn't see her.'

Shuffling along the dam, Kelvin prised out a piece of corrugated iron which was acting as a sluice gate. The river slid through the gap like a great eel, leaving the rock dry. Walking back along the dam, he collected a dustpan and brush from the bank while the commander picked up the coffee jar containing the hoard. On their hands and knees, they carefully scraped out the crevices in the rock.

'Bit of gravel mixed in,' commented Kelvin. 'Perhaps we ought to block some of the holes in the dam and get more water coming down.'

'If there was no gravel at all, it would mean we were almost certainly losing some gold as well. I think we've got it about right.'

Malcolm came squeaking over with another barrowload. 'Can't you tell those bikers of yours to turn the music down?'

'I think it's quite nice,' replied Kelvin.

'I'm not worried about the aesthetics of it, but you can hear it for miles and I think it's attracting the others.'

'What others?' asked the commander.

'The other people who've turned up,' said Malcolm patiently.

'Christ!' exclaimed Kelvin. Dropping his dustpan, he scrabbled up the bank, the commander close behind.

They looked back towards the gravel pit where Ivor was still grinding away with his tractor. The yellow arm of the digger was waving in the air, but the tractor itself was hull-down in the middle of the field 50 yards away. Surrounding it were thirty bobbing torsos and, beyond, people were walking across the field from the road.

'Where did they come from?' demanded Kelvin.

'They've only just started turning up,' replied Malcolm. 'They've all heard there's been a gold strike and have come to try their luck.'

'Why hasn't one of you cleared them off?'

'Ivor tried, but they won't go.'

'Well, get the police!'

'Why?'

'Trespass!'

'That's not a criminal offence. Anyway, Percy's on holiday and we'd need Archie before we could do anything. He's the land owner and, of course, he's gone back to London.'

Kelvin began to breathe heavily. 'I'll go and get my gun.'

'Now that would be a criminal offence.'

'Well, I'm not going to stand here and do nothing. Follow me!'

Kelvin strode up the river bank, the commander and Malcolm tagging along behind. They reached the edge of the Great Hole. The damp gravel was exposed in a large elliptical scar biting deep into the field.

Kelvin accosted one of the new arrivals, a young man picking through a small heap of gravel he had carried to the edge of the

Hole. Occasionally moistening a finger, he would dab at a piece of grit to examine it more closely.

'Where have you lot come from?' Kelvin asked.

The young man looked up. 'Hullo. Isn't it exciting? Are you one of the ones that got here first? We're an outing from the county library. We were going to go on a coach trip round the moor but we heard about this.'

'Are those from the library too?' asked Kelvin, waving his hand in the direction of a motley collection of senior citizens, dot-and-carrying their way across the field towards them.

'No. They're from a home for retired licensed victuallers. Their coach arrived in the car park by the bridge just as we were walking away. It's lucky you've got that music on, otherwise we wouldn't have known where exactly to come.'

'Hmph!' grunted Kelvin, turning back to his companions. 'I think it's time we did something about this.'

'What?' asked the commander.

'You're a spineless bugger!' sneered Kelvin.

'No, I'm not. There's just nothing we can do without Archie.'

'I'm not giving up the best chance I've had all my life to make some easy money. The gold's in our parish and it's ours, not these outsiders'.'

'What you mean is you want the lot,' said Malcolm.

'That's right, but you can have some too.'

'I agree with the commander. There's nothing we can do without Archie.'

'You've forgotten our little Rupert and his chums,' replied Kelvin. 'You remember what we thought when he came over the river at us? All we need to do is get him over here to scowl at them librarians and the geriatrics and they'll be off across the field as fast as their little legs can carry them. Then we can put Rupert in the car park waving dead chickens and axe handles in a casual sort of way and we'll be left in peace. Otherwise, I can see most of the county's going to be here before the day's out. Follow me!'

They followed him.

'See what I mean?' said Kelvin as they walked along the edge of the pit.

It looked as if Kelvin was on to something. Raucous music blared across the countryside from the bank where the Angels were sitting. The newcomers crowded the far end of the scar, keeping as far away from the anarchic threat as possible. One speaker was hooked to a rumbling motor cycle, the other was in the river with Rupert. Walking over to the motor bike, Kelvin pulled the wires from the battery and then switched off the engine.

The ex-beautician turned to see who was responsible for the sudden silence. Stretching her leather-clad limbs, she smiled, her nose ring cocking itself against her nostril – an effect that must have taken much practice.

'Hullo, Kelvin,' she said. 'What'y'want to turn it off for?'

'I've got a job for you lot. I want you to go and rip off a few chicken heads and snarl at all these people. I want them off this land. I'll provide the chickens.' He frowned. 'Rupert! What are you doing with that thing?'

Rupert was doing his speaker no good at all. Repeatedly plunging it into the water, he kept examining the bottom with the absorbed air of a primate searching for titbits in a companion's armpit.

'I've cracked it!' he called.

Turning back to Dawn, Kelvin gestured towards the river. 'What's he talking about?'

'He's discovered some magic way of finding gold. It's boring,' said Dawn.

Rupert sloshed his way to the bank, kicking aside a well-bedded boulder that tried to trip him. 'Look at this! It's great!'

'Look at what?'

'The bottom of the speaker. It's covered in gold!'

Kelvin knelt to examine the brandished object. 'Bugger me!' he exclaimed. 'It is! How'd you do that?'

'I thought of it all by myself. The bottom of this thing's a magnet, see? And I saw it picked up a bit of glittery stuff when I put it on the bank. So I put it into the river and shoogled it round in the gravel and it picked up all this. Not bad, hey?'

'Not bad? It's bloody marvellous! Do you see all that, Commander? That's very good, Rupert. You're a very clever lout.'

'Oh God!' said the commander.

'What's wrong?' asked Kelvin, turning to the commander. 'You've gone a very funny colour. You're not having a heart attack?'

The commander coughed apologetically. 'Kelvin, old chap, I wonder if I might have a quiet word – in private?'

'In private? I've no secrets from my lads.' His expansive gesture encompassed all four Angels.

'In private, Kelvin,' repeated the commander firmly. Taking Kelvin by the elbow, he pulled him out of earshot of the Angels. Malcolm followed, looking as grim as the commander.

'What do you want?' asked Kelvin. 'We can't waste time. There are more people coming across the field.'

'This is rather difficult, Kelvin, but do you remember that chat we had in the pub? About whether this stuff was gold or not?'

'Yes,' replied Kelvin impatiently. 'What about it?'

'And we concluded there was no way we could tell without expert help? Well, there is a way.'

'Oh. And what's that?'

'Gold is not magnetic. Iron pyrites is.'

'You mean this stuff's fool's gold?'

'That's right,' said the commander gently.

'Malcolm? D'y'think the commander's right?'

'Yes.'

'Shit!' Kelvin stared at his feet for a few seconds. 'Shit!' he repeated. 'Tell me, Commander, have these iron pyrites got any value at all?'

'None, I'm afraid.'

'Hmm. Bit of a blow.' Kelvin rubbed his stubbly chin, deep in thought.

'It is,' agreed the commander. 'But you're taking it very well.'

'All is not lost,' responded Kelvin. 'It just requires a bit of a change of approach.' He went back towards Rupert. 'You're doing a great job, sunshine. Get back in the river and pull out more gold, but let out strange and terrifying cries if anybody comes over to see what you're doing. We don't want anyone to find out your secret, do we?'

Rupert pursed his lips. 'Strange and terrifying cries? I'm not so sure I know any.'

'You big nellie! Just be yourself. Roar at them and give them a dirty look.'

'All right! There's no need to get narky.' He turned to Malcolm and the commander. 'Kelvin gets very narky, you know.'

'Yes, we know,' said Malcolm.

'With all the problems life loads upon my shoulders, it'd be a miracle if I didn't,' said Kelvin. 'It's up to me to salvage something from this mess.'

'What mess?' queried Rupert.

'Never you mind. Just concentrate on getting gold and being strange and terrifying.'

'Right!' said Rupert. He scowled experimentally.

'Bloody good!' said Kelvin, taking an involuntary step backwards. 'But wait until we've gone.'

The commander and Malcolm trotted after him. 'I don't see what we can do, Kelvin,' said Malcolm.

'Lucky you've got me to look after our interests then, isn't it?' They were heading back towards the mass of prospectors. Kelvin put his hand inside his jacket and pulled out the jam jar containing the fruit of their morning's work. 'We'll just see what we can do with this.'

'But it's worthless, Kelvin. It's iron pyrites.'

'That's just your opinion.'

'What's that supposed to mean?'

'It means I ain't gone to all this trouble for nothing.'

'What are you up to?'

Kelvin gave a confident smile. 'Just you wait and see.'

Casually playing with the jar of gold, Kelvin looked out across the grovelling multitude in the Great Hole. Some had had the sense to wear gumboots but many were splashing about in ordinary shoes with the mud up to their knees. The senior citizens were in a quarrelsome group, arguing for possession of a magnifying glass, their only hope of spying the glitter amid the dross.

Kelvin stepped down into the pit and paddled over to them. 'Morning!' he called.

They turned to examine him before dismissing him to continue their argument. 'There ain't no point in hanging on to the

glass, Mary,' said a wiry old lady wearing a brooch inscribed 'Nanny' on her lapel. 'Your eyesight's so bad that you can't even read the label on a gin bottle any more.'

'You give it to me, Mary,' said an old man with a rheumy blue eye and matching anorak. 'I can still read without glasses.'

'Looking for gold ain't like looking at dirty magazines, George Prescott,' said another. 'We're here to get rich. I think we should give the glass to the bus driver. He should have decent eyesight. Where's he gone, anyway?'

'He went off. He said it was every man for himself.'

Kelvin winked at the commander. Holding the jar in the air, he shook it. The contents rattled against the tin lid.

'What you got there?' demanded George Prescott.

'This?' said Kelvin, looking down at the jam jar as if he had just seen it for the first time. 'This?'

'Yes. That!'

Kelvin waited until all eyes were on the jar. 'We got it out of the river this morning,' he said, vaguely. 'It's this 'ere stuff that everybody's looking for. That's right, isn't it, Malcolm?'

'Er . . . yes,' agreed Malcolm.

'Let's have a look,' demanded George. 'Give me the magnifying glass, Mary!' Mary handed over her magnifying glass without protest. Kelvin, keeping a tight hold on the jar, unscrewed the lid allowing George to bend over to squint at the contents. 'Bloody hell! It is!'

'Is it?' said Kelvin, replacing the lid. 'Us here don't rightly know about things like this.' He gave an unconvincing laugh. 'Bullocks. Now I can tell 'ee a lot about bullocks. But this stuff . . .' He pursed his lips and shook his head. 'Do you know what?'

'What?'

Kelvin lowered his voice. 'Some say this is gold!'

A senescent at the back of the crowd nudged his neighbour. 'What's 'ee say?'

'Sorry!' Kelvin raised his voice. 'They say this is gold.' He held the jar above his head to show that the contents were yellow and glittery.

'Keep your voice down!' exclaimed George, looking fearfully round at the other prospectors.

'No, speak up,' contradicted Mary. 'We want to hear too.'

'What I was wondering . . .' Again Kelvin let his voice trail away.

'Wondering?' prompted George.

'Yes, I was wondering if any of you city types would know how to sell gold. Us country people don't know anything about that sort of thing. I can sell corn and cattle, but you can't take gold to market.'

'You're asking us?' asked George Prescott.

'Yes.'

'Would you let me and my friends have a little talk first?'

'A little talk?' Kelvin wrinkled his brow. 'I just want some advice. If you don't know, I can easily go and ask someone else.'

'No, don't do that!' exclaimed George hastily. 'Just wait over there a minute.' He pointed to the edge of the Hole a few yards away.

Kelvin shrugged. Putting the jar back in his pocket, he ambled over. The commander, gnawing at his moustache, and

Malcolm followed faithfully. *Voce*, not as *sotto* as it might have been, rose from the bus party. The others pretended not to hear.

George turned. 'Come back here!'

Kelvin came. So did his entourage.

'You think we're stupid, don't you?' said George.

Kelvin smiled.

'Well, we're not. We can see your little game. I bet this whole thing is illegal, isn't it? And you want us to take the risk when the gold is sold?'

Kelvin tried a rueful grin. 'Ah, well, I can see I under-estimated you. I'll let you get on with your own prospecting.' He turned to go.

'No, wait! Don't be in such a hurry!'

Kelvin stopped. 'But you know what I'm up to!'

'Yes. It doesn't mean we can't do business, all the same. We can dig our own gold, of course, but we're quite willing to help you out. If the price is right.'

'Would you?' said Kelvin. 'That would be very kind of you.'

'Do you know what it's worth?' asked George.

'No. It's got to be quite a lot, though.' He pulled out his jar and shook it once more. The eyes of the bus party fixed upon it.

'Before she ran a pub, Jean used to work for a jeweller,' said George. 'She ought to be able to put a fair price on it.'

'Will she, by God!' said Kelvin.

Jean was produced at the front of the bus party. Kelvin was relieved to see that she was very, very old. Taking a pair of spectacles from her handbag, she placed them on her nose and examined the grit, poking it with a skeletal forefinger.

'Never saw anything like this in my day,' she said. 'Wedding rings. We saw a lot of those, especially in the Depression.'

'But what's gold worth?' asked George.

'Five guineas an ounce. That's what Mr Stanley used to pay. But that's the price for pure gold and most of the items we received were only 9 carat. I don't know what this is.' She looked optimistically up at Kelvin. 'You haven't found a hallmark, have you? That would be a great help. Gold can be very confusing, you know. It could be plated or it could be rolled gold. A hallmark would tell us exactly what it was.'

The commander gave a low moan and tugged at Kelvin's

sleeve. 'We can't take advantage of these people,' he whispered in Kelvin's ear.

'Shut up and mind your own business!' replied Kelvin.

'Anyway, without a hallmark it's very difficult to say just what kind of gold this is. But 5 guineas was what we paid.'

Malcolm coughed. 'Er . . . I think you'll find that prices are slightly different now.'

'Oh yes,' agreed George. 'I'm sure that things are different, but that gives us a figure to work on.'

'I can remember a more up-to-date price,' said Malcolm.

'Thank God for that!' said Kelvin.

'I think Jean's is quite adequate for our purposes,' said George, trying to quell Malcolm with a frown.

'Eight hundred dollars an ounce was the last figure I can recall,' said Malcolm firmly.

'Malcolm!' exclaimed the commander.

'How about £12 an ounce?' suggested George.

'Fifty,' said Kelvin.

'Thirty?'

'Fifty.'

'I don't want anything to do with this,' said the commander abruptly.

'Really?' said Kelvin. 'I'll have that in writing?'

'Why?'

'Malcolm, you're the witness. The commander wants nothing to do with this and further transactions. He wishes to renounce his share of any profits.'

'Yes, I heard.'

'This is immoral,' said the commander. 'I'm not going to stand for it!'

'Shut up, Commander,' ordered Kelvin.

'Yes. Shut up,' agreed George Prescott. 'Have you got anything that would weigh out an ounce properly?'

'It's an ounce troy,' said Jean, 'not an ounce avoirdupois.'

'I'll tell you what,' said Kelvin. 'How about if I sell you the whole jar? There's got to be a fair bit in here.' He hefted it, grunting to show the effort. 'How about £500 for the whole lot?'

George looked round at the rest of the bus party. 'I haven't got that sort of money. But perhaps if we could club together?'

'That's an excellent idea,' said Malcolm. 'You ought to split it up into fifty lots and sell them at £10 each. Then you and your friends can each invest as much as you want.'

Kelvin looked at Malcolm admiringly. 'You've a bit of a talent for this sort of thing.'

'Give us a few minutes and we'll come up with the money,' said George. 'Fifty lots at £5 each.'

'Done!' said Kelvin.

George led his group to the edge of the Hole, where they assisted each other on to the grass. A financial bacchanalia developed, currency being fished from elderly bloomers and neat purses as well as wallets.

'I think this is shocking!' said the commander. 'I might have expected this sort of thing from you, Kelvin. But, Malcolm, you're a teacher and supposed to be an example to the young!'

'Here!' The shout came from a man in his forties wearing a red tracksuit and gumboots. 'You with the silly moustache!' The commander looked round. 'Yes, you. I've been watching you lot. I want a word!'

'Is that individual addressing me?' inquired the commander frostily, watching the man abandon his little pile of gravel, which he was sifting with the aid of a tyre brace, and walk towards them.

'You're the only person with a silly moustache,' replied Kelvin.

'Are you selling gold, mate?' asked the man. He had a strong London accent.

'I am not your mate. Nor am I selling gold. In fact, why don't you clear off!' The commander squared his shoulders and surveyed the vicinity. 'We ought to get rid of this rabble completely!'

'Hark at you!' said the stranger. 'If you don't watch your tongue, I'll rearrange your moustache. With this!' He waved the brace in the commander's face.

The commander did not flinch. The eye that had swept the Spanish Main from the deck of a frigate, after a courtesy visit to Miami, looked bleakly back at the aggressor. 'Will you, now?'

'Yes, I will. I don't want any trouble but I want some of that gold. I'll give you a decent price. You lot seem to be the only people who are organized on this.'

The commander turned his Arctic eye towards Kelvin. 'I've

reconsidered my position, Kelvin. I'm with you again. In fact, I think I'll get back to the river and make sure we can get enough for our friend here. I'll bring Rupert back as well.'

'Very wise,' said Kelvin approvingly.

'That's a bit more like it.' The man lowered the tyre brace. 'I'll make you an offer you can't refuse.'

'I'm sure we won't,' agreed the commander. 'I'm sure we'll be able to sell you as much as you like.'

At the end of the day, the pub was subdued.

'I'm not altogether happy about this business,' said Lindy.

'I thought we were going to get really rich,' said Jimmy, depressed. 'Not just make a couple of grand.'

'Come on!' scoffed Bill. 'You didn't seriously expect there to be gold just waiting to be picked up, did you?'

'Yes,' said Jimmy sadly.

'I must admit that I did too,' said Kelvin. 'But it was me that organized the auction up on the road. If it hadn't been for me, we'd have made nothing.'

'I wasn't at all happy about that,' said the commander.

'I was absolutely straight. I never said it was gold, and if it hadn't have been for Rupert some of those bastards would've mugged us for it.'

'What'll we do with the money?' asked the commander.

'Give it to the village hall fund,' said Lindy promptly. 'Then we could begin on the foundations.'

'I didn't put in all that work to give it to the village hall,' said Kelvin. 'That gold was supposed to be my pay-off for Brett.'

'Archie's going to do his nut when he sees the mess we've made,' said Ivor.

'I'll just say it's a bit of deep ploughing,' said Kelvin.

'Okay. So even if he doesn't sue you, what are you going to say to the people when they ask for their money back?'

Malcolm agreed. 'The bus party was one thing, but that fellow with the iron bar is going to be most unhappy when he tries to sell his gold.'

'That's what I mean,' said Lindy. 'He can smack you on the nose and demand his money back, but it won't do him much good to beat up the village hall.'

178

Mick came crashing through the door, rubbing his hands. 'Evening all!'

'Why are you so happy?' asked Kelvin. 'You didn't even make the river.'

'We've got a gold rush in progress. I thought there might be visitors about. We've been taking a fortune at the café!'

'It's like a cave or a beach!' said Jimmy. 'You know. We said Moorcombe needed a special attraction and that was it!'

'It's been bloody marvellous!' said Mick. 'And guess what? Prudence was in this morning. Apparently Archie wanted to stick a pond there and get it dug out for free!'

The pub was silent.

'You mean the whole business was Archie conning us to dig his boating lake for him?' said Kelvin.

'That's right.'

Kelvin sighed. 'The clever sod! He's bloody had us!' But then he brightened. 'Still, we've all done all right. He got his pond, Mick flogged his ice creams and we've come out with a bit of money.'

'Brett'll be all right too,' said Lindy. 'His father looks to be as big a crook as you!'

Kelvin smiled with pride. 'Yes, Brett's going to be a right chip off the old block, ain't he?'

Chapter Nine

Wildfowling

'STANLEY COHEN'S been chasing after me again,' remarked Kelvin with a cough.

With the onset of cold weather, stoicism was required to endure the public bar of the Hunted Hind. Smoky all the year round, its atmosphere deteriorated still further when a fire was first lit at the end of the summer in the huge open hearth. It took a month before patrons became used to it.

'He's been on to me too,' said Bill. 'He always is at this time of year.'

'Stanley Cohen?' asked the commander delicately. 'One of the Cohens of Glencoe?'

'I wouldn't know about that,' said Bill. 'I don't know Glencoe. 'T'ain't one of the farms round here. He made a lot of money in the motor trade and bought Ravenridge about six years ago after old Lady Huxtable died. You know him, surely. He's the one who does the shooting.'

'Oh, yes. I know,' said the commander with a curl to his lip. With the first frost, he had put on his down-filled waistcoat and his heaviest tweed trousers. Together with his old school tie, rather too garish to be out of the topmost drawer, these would remain his uniform until May.

'Well, I don't,' said Malcolm.

'He has all those foreigners down to shoot pheasants. Pretty bad form, really.'

'What's bad form about it?'

'Oh, they're good pheasants,' said Ivor, who reared fifty birds a year which he released on his farm. 'High and very fast, I believe. But he guarantees to put at least a thousand over the guns in a day. That was all very well fifty years ago, but it's not really on now. All these environmental types don't like it and it's not very sporting.'

'It must cost him a fortune!' exclaimed the commander.

'It certainly makes him one. He puts down 140,000 birds with only two full-time keepers and charges the punters £16 a bird. Plus VAT.'

'It's a full-blown industry!' said the commander. 'He must be rolling in it! How much land has he got?'

'A hundred acres,' said Kelvin sourly. 'But he rents the shooting rights over half the county. You used to be able to have a day out with a gun almost anywhere round here. But he's gone and put his bloody birds down all over the place. He reckons he could have a couple of very nice drives across the combe between Bill's farm and mine on the north side. Cheeky bugger!'

Kelvin took a long pull on his beer. He emitted a satisfied belch, raising frowns on a late pair of elderly tourists whose car, complete with stickers from the National Trust and the Civil Service Motoring Association, was parked outside.

'He's also gone and got the rights on my cousin Abraham's farm above the reservoir,' continued Kelvin. 'That's a real tragedy.'

'Why is that such a tragedy?' asked the commander.

'The geese. At the right time of year, geese come in to the reservoir and Abraham's farm is right on their flight line.'

Bill suddenly became animated. 'D'y'remember, Kelvin? It was real exciting in the old days when we were out there at dusk or before dawn waiting for them. Then we'd hear that honking and the whistle of their wings as they came over.' The light died from his eyes. 'That was quite something in the old days.'

'Damn right!' agreed Kelvin with feeling. 'Greylag geese, they were. We don't get them down here no more. It's Canada geese now, hundreds of them!'

'I haven't been after geese for years,' said Ivor.

'I shot a duck once,' contributed the commander, 'and I did get Donald.'

Donald had been a domesticated Canada goose which had terrorized the village until the commander had succeeded in squashing it with his car.

'Is it all right to shoot Canada geese?' continued the

commander. 'Isn't it a bit like shooting pandas or fishing for Mandy's shubunkin in her pond?'

'They taste jolly good and give you an interesting shot if they're not too tame,' said Ivor.

'That's not quite what I meant,' said the commander.

'It would be nice to go out once more before I die,' said Jimmy from his chair.

'I'd like to try too,' said Archie Spontini. 'I used to like that sort of thing when I was younger. Mum never actually let me have a gun, but I sometimes shot hens with my catapult.'

Having won grudging respect from the natives over his pond, Archie's moon face was now a regular sight in the pub. He had not yet graduated to a bar stool, but he often shared Annie's bench by the window under the moth-eaten stag's head. Instead of the stained tweed jackets and green army surplus sweaters favoured by the others, he was wearing a Fair Isle jersey and cavalry twill trousers.

'Well, you can't,' said Kelvin. 'Stanley's got the rights.'

At a table by the fireplace, the tourists were having trouble with the scampi-in-the-basket that they had ordered for lunch.

'I've got an idea,' said Jimmy, looking at the floor with modest pride.

The commander sighed. 'Tell us about it, Jimmy.'

'Well, I was thinking if Kelvin and Bill and Archie said they were considering letting their shooting and then asked for a morning or two out after geese, Stanley Cohen would likely give his permission just to keep them sweet.'

'But I just said I don't want to let my shooting, you silly old bugger!' exclaimed Kelvin.

'Don't you call me a silly old bugger!'

'Well, you are one.'

'No he's not!' interrupted Bill. 'That's not a bad idea at all. We don't have to have any intention of actually coming to an agreement. But I know he wants our shooting badly. I think it's worth a try.'

Ivor shifted on his stool. 'Er . . . if you do get the nod, you will insist that you make up a party, won't you? I'd love to come.'

'Me too,' said the commander eagerly.

'Of course,' said Bill.

'It's not "of course" at all,' said Kelvin. 'A bit of goose shooting is bound to be worth money. We'd be silly just to give it away.'

'You forget it's not your land, Kelvin,' said Ivor. 'Remember you've got my trailer as well as Bill's saw and the commander's concrete mixer. We could always take them back.'

'That's right,' said Bill. 'And Archie's kin as well as your next-door neighbour.'

'Archie's not going to wave a gun around anywhere near me.' warned Kelvin.

'I certainly won't come,' said Malcolm.

'You're not being asked,' said Kelvin.

'Who's going to phone up Cohen?' asked the commander.

'Bill,' said Kelvin.

'Ivor,' said Bill.

'It was Jimmy's idea,' said Annie with a cackle.

'I haven't got a telephone,' said Jimmy.

The pub lapsed into silence and stools swivelled to inspect the progress of the scampi which was still being dissected. The man, an expression of bemused incredulity on his face, was sawing vainly at the bogey-like chunk of matter nestling coyly inside the battered breadcrumbs.

'There's a good hundredweight of that stuff still in the freezer,' remarked Kelvin.

'They tried some of it on the cat, but it died,' added Jimmy.

The commander frowned. 'Be fair. The animal had distemper or something.'

'If you were offered that stuff, would it make you feel better or worse?' asked Kelvin.

'Yes . . .' mused the commander. 'It can't be doing much for trade.'

'If you ask me, that's no bad thing,' said Ivor. 'Anything that discourages tourists meets with my approval.'

None of those round the bar made their living from visitors and they grunted agreement.

'I've got an idea!' said Jimmy again. The pub looked at him warily. 'I'll ring Cohen from here!'

'What? Now?' asked the commander.

'If I use the phone in here, it means I won't have to go out to the call box later on,' he said. Heaving himself to his feet, he shuffled round the bar to the telephone. 'Does anyone know the number?'

'Look it up,' said the commander. 'There's a book down there somewhere.'

'Would you look it up? I haven't got my glasses with me.' This was the code used by the more old-fashioned locals to indicate that literacy was not their strong point. Ivor obliged, printing the numerals on a beer mat.

Jimmy dialled gingerly. 'Hullo? Can I speak to Mr Cohen? Sorry? Could you speak up a bit? My hearing's not as good as it was. Sorry? Hullo? Hullo?' He put his hand over the receiver. 'I think the bugger's hung up. What do I do now?'

'Let's have a listen,' said Kelvin, leaning across the bar to take the telephone. 'There's nobody there, you fool!'

'Well, there was.'

'Give me the phone and I'll do it.'

Kelvin dialled, waiting until the instrument at the other end was ringing before handing back the receiver.

'Hullo? Hullo? Speak up, you silly bastard!' Jimmy looked angrily back at Kelvin. 'He's hung up again!'

'I bet it's you, you silly old sod. I'll take over . . .' Snatching the receiver, Kelvin re-dialled. There was a pause, disturbed only by angry mutterings from Jimmy. 'It's an answering machine,' said Kelvin. 'They've got one at the AI Centre. You've got to be able to handle new-fangled technology if you're going to get anywhere these days. Hullo? Could you tell Mr Cohen that we want to shoot his geese. Actually, I don't mean they're his geese. Those geese that cross the field where they're always trying to grow swedes on their way to the pond.'

Bill nudged him in the ribs. 'Bugger off,' said Kelvin. 'No, not you,' he said to the telephone. 'It's Bill who's just poked me. Hang on a second.' He covered the receiver with his hand. 'What do you want?'

'He won't know what you mean by the pond. It was a reservoir before he got here. He'll probably think you're talking about his duck pond.'

'And why should geese grow swedes on their way there?' asked the commander in puzzlement.

Kelvin glanced from one to the other.

'Look,' he growled. 'It's me that's making this call. You

make your own if you want to.' He returned to the telephone. 'Where was I? Oh, of course, you won't tell me. Anyway, we'll be coming out some morning, probably next Thursday if the weather's not bad, to have a go at them geese and he can come and talk to us about renting the shooting on our farms. I'm not promising – hullo? hullo?' He put the telephone back on its cradle. 'The bloody thing's hung up on me! Well, I was about finished anyway.'

'You didn't say who was calling,' said Ivor.

'Yes, I did.'

'Ivor's right,' said the commander. 'You didn't.'

'All right, I'll phone it back.' He dialled again. 'It's engaged. Anyway it doesn't matter even if I didn't say. It just means he may not know who to come and chat up about renting shooting and that I don't mind.'

'If he doesn't know who phoned up, then he won't know who's going to shoot the geese and he may accuse us of poaching.'

'Nonsense,' replied Kelvin airily. 'He's only been here a few years and he's got no more rights than us. Geese aren't like pheasants, you know. He doesn't rear them or pay money for them. If there's any problems, I'll take responsibility.'

Ivor sighed. 'I can't think why, but that does not fill me with confidence.'

When the shootists mustered, the sky showed only the tiniest hint that there could be another day struggling up from behind the hills. As they emerged from their vehicles into the drizzle, not all of them were showing the proper degree of excited anticipation.

'I must be bloody mad!' exclaimed Ivor, peering round at the muddy gateway in the light of Kelvin's handlamp. 'I got out of a nice warm bed for this.'

'Have you told Abraham that we're here?' asked Bill.

'No,' replied Kelvin. 'It's Cohen's business, not his.'

'But won't he wonder what's going on when we start firing?' asked Archie. He was resplendent in a new gentleman's out-door jacket and deerstalker, but the effect was spoiled by the rusticity of the Middlecott shotgun which had stained his green-waxed arm red with rust.

'The house is across the other side of the hill. He won't be able to hear us.'

Kelvin indicated the hill by spotlighting a startled hind quarter of a mile away. Slicing wildly through the drizzle, the beam ended up across the field through the gateway. 'We're going to line up along that hedge.' The beam snapped up and down the hedgebank which ran at right angles to the road 100 yards further along. 'And I'm putting you right down at the bottom of the field, Archie.'

Archie looked across the muddy black immensity of the swede field. 'I don't see why it has to be me that goes all the way down there.'

'Because somebody has to and none of the rest of us want a load of swanshot up our arses,' replied Kelvin.

'How long do we have to stay here?' asked Archie.

'You don't *have* to stay at all,' said Bill. 'This is supposed to be a treat, not a duty. But the geese should come over in dribs and drabs until full daylight.'

'That's right,' replied Kelvin. 'If you don't want to come, you can piss off.'

'All right, Kelvin, I didn't mean any offence,' replied Archie, kicking the wheel of the Land Rover.

'And don't kick my Land Rover!' Kelvin glared at him and then turned back to the others. 'Right! How many of you lot have shot geese before?'

Ivor had. The commander hadn't. Bill had. Archie had with his catapult, once, and Jimmy hadn't turned up at all.

'What we're going to do is spread out along the ditch. You've got to get right into it and lean up against the hedge. They're canny birds, geese, and if they have any hint of anyone waiting to shoot them, they won't come near us.'

'How will we know when they come over if we're supposed to have our noses pressed in the hedge?' asked Archie. 'Do we shoot them up the arse when they've gone past or something?'

'The whistle of the wings and the honking,' said Bill. 'When you hear . . .'

'Yes. We had all that bit in the pub the other day,' interrupted Kelvin. 'It's as Bill says. When you hear them coming and when you reckon they're just about up to you, then you fire. Any other questions?' Kelvin set night vision back by ten minutes by flashing his lightsabre into the eyes of those around him. 'Right then! Let's get into position.'

It is a masochist's pleasure to stand waist-deep in a ditch with one's nose pressed against the thorny skeletons of a winter-killed tangle of brambles. Their tendrils take advantage of the darkness to edge stealthily towards unprotected flesh and sink in their hard grey claws. Muffled swearing from Ivor, who was stationed in the middle of the line, indicated that he was not of that persuasion.

'What's wrong?' whispered the commander, who was 20 yards further along the ditch.

'These damn brambles!'

'Shut up!' blared Kelvin from his position by the road.

'Commander!' Ivor had lowered his voice to a hoarse whisper.

'Yes?'

'Did you bring a flask?'

'Only coffee,' apologized his companion. 'And I've left that in my car.'

'Blast!' Ivor began a low litany of complaint as he tried to disentangle himself.

'Shut up!' yelled Kelvin again.

He was answered by a frantic series of honkings from the other side of the hedge as a drib or a drab of intended prey opened air brakes, adjusted flaps, viffed and made a rapid change of course. There were sounds of poorly muffled laughter from down the line.

'Now see what you've done!' Kelvin bellowed. 'You've got to keep quiet!' A second flight of Canada geese honked their dismay as his cow-calling voice alerted them. 'Shit!'

The hunters fell damply silent as the sky gradually turned grey, revealing curtains of drizzle drifting down the heather-clad hillside and across the fields towards them. The commander eased his way along the ditch until he was beside Ivor. 'This is bloody boring,' he said. 'I can't believe Cohen's punters pay good money to do this.'

'I used to go after greylags in Scotland and it was a damn sight worse, I can assure you. I've been out with snow driving into my face. At least it's not that cold.'

'I'm cold,' said the commander gloomily, 'and I'm wet.'

'Don't be so pathetic,' replied Ivor. A quartet of geese honked their way over the commander's vacated position. Ivor clicked his tongue in exasperation. 'Now look what's happened! If you'd been where you were supposed to be, you'd've been able to take a shot at those.'

There was a sudden fusillade from Bill and Archie to the right of the line. It was still dark enough to see the stabs of fire from the barrels of the guns.

Ivor stiffened with excitement. 'Did you get anything?' he called softly.

Bill's voice came floating back. 'No, they flew over Archie.'

Kelvin exploded almost immediately, a single shot, a yell of triumph and he rose from the ditch into the field. 'I got one! I got one!'

'He got one, he got one,' echoed the commander sourly.

'Can we go home now?' shouted Archie, climbing out of his hide and turning towards Kelvin. 'Hey! Look over there!'

They looked.

Running across the field towards their ditch was a man with a gun. He was making slow progress, since the treacly clay subsoil had been brought to the surface through careless ploughing by Cousin Abraham. As the shootists watched his laborious approach, a white Land Rover bounced through the gateway and stalled. Its starter churned feebly.

The commander and Ivor clambered out of the ditch. 'That must be Cohen's gamekeeper,' said the commander uncertainly. 'It doesn't look as if Kelvin's message got through. I hope this is not going to be embarrassing.'

'Oh, no. It'll be all right. Kelvin said it was his party and he's a difficult man to embarrass. It's his cousin's farm, anyway.'

The vehicle was moving again, crawling cautiously through the swedes, its wavering lights losing their intensity against the dawn. The putative keeper stopped while he was still 50 yards away.

'Put down your guns!'

'I most certainly will not!' responded Ivor. 'It's a Holland and Holland and I'm not going to get it wet and muddy. Kelvin! Do something!'

Kelvin was half-way through the hedge towards his prey and entangled in the brambles.

188

'You!' shouted the keeper. 'It's no good! You can't escape!'

'I'm not trying to escape, you stupid bastard!' roared Kelvin. 'I'm stuck. And who the hell do you think you are? You're trespassing!'

'That's my boy,' murmured Ivor comfortably.

'Trespassing!' The man had short-cropped hair and a Midlands accent. Kelvin's response seemed to annoy him. 'Bloody poachers! You come down off that hedge immediately. And the rest of you! Come slowly towards me.'

The Land Rover drew up behind him and the driver emerged. 'We've got you this time!' said the gamekeeper, turning to his reinforcement. 'Red-handed! I told you there was a gang working the area, Constable!'

'Morning, Percy,' said Kelvin.

'Morning, Kelvin,' said Percy.

'Do you know this man, Constable?' asked the gamekeeper.

'Course he does,' said Kelvin. 'I'm a prominent citizen in these parts. If you did your job properly, you'd know me too.'

'I don't give a damn who you are. I've caught you and your henchmen.'

'Henchmen?' Ivor wrinkled his brow at the commander. 'I've been called many things in my time but I don't recall ever being called a henchman.'

'Don't let's be too hasty here.' Percy was uneasily aware that his best pair of boots was sinking slowly into the clay beneath his feet. He was fidgeting.

'What's wrong with you, Percy?' asked Kelvin. 'You look as if you've wet your pants.'

'Arrest them, for heaven's sake!'

'Now hold on a minute!' Percy raised a conciliatory hand. 'If there's any offences been committed, I'll make sure the culprit faces the due process of the law, but you can't rush these things.'

'What are you talking about? Do your job, man. Arrest them!'

'Look Mr Baldwick . . .'

'Baldwick!' sneered Kelvin.

'You keep your mouth shut, Kelvin Morchard!' snapped Percy. 'Any stirring from you and I will run you in!'

Kelvin opened his mouth, thought better of it and concentrated instead on disentangling himself from the hedge.

Percy turned towards the others. 'Commander, you look like a sensible man. Can you explain your presence here with firearms?'

'Well, it was Kelvin's idea. He used to shoot geese here when he was a child, so he phoned up Mr Cohen and asked his permission.'

'Bullsh—'

Percy cut Baldwick short with a peremptory gesture.

'You've been eating your spinach, this morning, Percy,' remarked Ivor admiringly.

'Kelvin, can you prove you asked permission?'

'Course I can prove it. Virtually everyone here heard me make the phone call. Although it's a funny world when you have to ask some stranger permission to do something you've been doing for years. And on land owned by your own family.'

'You may be right, Kelvin. But the law's the law.' Percy held up his hand again to quell more mutinous rumblings from the gamekeeper. 'You say you asked permission which we'll accept at this stage. Did Mr Cohen give you permission?'

'What do you mean?' asked Kelvin, skipping round the truth with the skill that comes from years of experience. 'I've just said that I phoned up. It was a tit for tat. Me and Bill were prepared to discuss letting out the shooting rights over our land in exchange.'

Percy turned to the gamekeeper and raised an enquiring eyebrow.

'I don't know anything about this,' said Baldwick, beginning to feel as if the situation were passing beyond his control. 'When did you speak to Mr Cohen?'

'Oh, it was last week some time,' replied Kelvin vaguely. He had finally fought free of the hedge and joined everyone else in the field.

'It can't have been last week because he's in Barbados.'

Kelvin scowled at Baldwick. 'Well, it may have been the week before, then.'

'He's been away for a month.'

This piece of information was assimilated in silence.

Percy shifted his feet again with a sigh. 'That's a pity. I suppose it's easy enough to prove?'

'Yes.'

'What have you got to say to that, Kelvin?'

'I certainly phoned him up. It's possible I spoke to one of those answering machines, but it's not my fault if the message was not passed on. That's right! It was one of those machines. I remember now. I left a message saying that I'd assume it would be okay to shoot unless he rang back and he didn't.' Kelvin turned towards the sullen dawn. 'Look, there's still another half-hour or so before the geese stop coming over. Can't we continue this conversation another time?'

'Bloody cheek!' exclaimed Baldwick indignantly.

'No, you can't, Kelvin. Whatever the rights and wrongs of this business, there's clearly some doubt about whether you're poaching or not. It would certainly be inappropriate if you continued shooting. By the way, I assume you've all got licences?'

'Of course,' replied Kelvin.

'Does that go for Mr Spontini as well?'

'Of course it does,' said Kelvin.

Percy looked thoughtfully at Archie who responded with a confident grin that would have led to a body search had he tried it on a customs officer. 'Hmm. Anyway, I think it best if you go home and we sort this business out later.'

'You're not going to let them get away with it?' exclaimed Baldwick with indignation. 'You're supposed to be a policeman and there's as blatant a breach of the law going on here as I've ever seen.'

'Don't tell me what to do or not to do,' said Percy, whose tether was not infinite.

'I wouldn't have to if you'd do your job. I worked in the Midlands before and there the police don't take the side of criminals.'

'Look, chum,' said Kelvin, 'your boss has been trying to get shooting on Bill's land and mine for years. You keep on like you're doing and I'll tell him he could have had it if you hadn't been such a prick.'

'What's your farm called?'

'Southcott.'

'Huh!' grunted Baldwick. 'That's the one outside the village with the river running through the valley?'

'That's it. Lovely drive it would make, wouldn't it? And Bill's got Northcott just above me. And Archie here, he's Middlecott.'

'And you're willing to give us the shooting?'

'If the price was right and if Archie doesn't turn his place into a boating lake. But I'm going to talk to your boss about it. I'm not going to discuss it with his hired help.'

'Watch it!' said Baldwick through narrowed eyes.

'Did you shoot anything?' asked Percy.

'I got one just before you lot turned up,' said Kelvin. 'I was going over the hedge to collect it when he started to shout at us. I'll go and get it now.'

'No, you won't. Even if you were paying for your gun, anything you shoot belongs to us,' said Baldwick.

'Don't be stupid!' replied Kelvin. 'I haven't come out here at this time of day to watch you walk away with my goose.'

Percy once again raised a magisterial hand. 'I'm afraid neither of you can have the goose. I'm going to have to impound it for evidence.'

'You can't do that!' said Baldwick indignantly.

'Look! Stop telling me what to do!'

'You tell him, Percy,' said Kelvin with approval.

'I'm telling you too. Go and get that goose!'

'Oh, all right! Keep your hair on.'

Kelvin's efforts to extricate himself from the brambles had created a motorway through the middle of the hedge which would not please Cousin Abraham although it might please his sheep. Kelvin pulled himself through the gap, beating at the brambles on the other side with the barrel of his gun, and disappeared.

'Can you see it, Kelvin?' called Percy. 'I don't want to have to stand here all day.'

'It's over in a boggy patch!' shouted Kelvin. 'I'll just go and pick it up . . . bugger me!'

The request sounded desperate.

'What's wrong?' asked Percy.

'Wrong? . . . er . . . there's nothing wrong. It's . . . er . . . just that the bird's landed right in a bog and it's covered in mud.'

'Oh well, hurry up.'

A couple of minutes later, Kelvin reappeared in the hedge bearing the remains of his victim. It needed faith to believe the bird ever had been a Canada goose. Its feathers were caked with greasy yellow clay.

Kelvin held it away from his body, shifting his grip on its legs from one hand to the other as they slid through his fingers. 'The bloody thing's a bit mucky, Percy,' he apologized. 'Will you take it so that I can go back to pick up my gun?'

Percy looked at the goose with distaste. 'No, thanks. I've a clean uniform on. You take it Baldwick. You're the one who wanted it so badly.'

'It's your evidence and you're not putting it in my Land Rover. My wife's taking it to the shops later this morning and she'll give me hell if there's mud all over the place.'

Kelvin made a generous gesture. 'I'll take it if you like, Percy. You don't really want it for evidence. Everyone here has seen it and can swear to it having been shot by me.'

'Hmm,' said Percy. He cocked an eye at the gamekeeper. 'Is that all right by you? If it isn't, you'll have to give me a lift with it back to the village.'

'It's all right by me,' said Baldwick hastily as Kelvin brought the dripping corpse towards him. 'But make sure you don't do any more shooting until I've had a word with Mr Cohen.'

'All right, Kelvin. You can take the goose. But I still need it as evidence. You can bring it round to the police house later on, after you've cleaned it up a bit.' Percy heaved one of his boots from the soil and looked mournfully down at the large quantity of the field adhering to it. 'I think we might as well go on home now.' Sitting down on the Land Rover's bumper, he scraped the mud carefully away with a variety of blades from his Swiss army knife.

Kelvin was not his usual self as he carried his goose back towards the road. He looked positively hunted as he joined the commander. 'Could I come back to your place before I go home?' he asked.

'Er . . . yes, of course. Ivor is coming back to forage with me for some breakfast. Please join us.' The commander was taken aback. Natives and immigrants of less than forty years' standing socialized in the pub and on formal occasions. But they were not prone to drop into each other's houses. 'Is there something wrong?'

'Yes.'

'Nothing serious?'

'It's serious.'

The commander patted Kelvin reassuringly on the back. 'Not to worry, we'll sort it out.'

'I hope so,' said Kelvin, but his voice lacked conviction.

'We've got Kelvin coming round for breakfast, as well. Apparently there's something wrong,' said the commander, scrutinizing the contents of the refrigerator. Instead of the usual goat's yoghurt and muesli laced with mouse turds, he was contemplating a feast of sausage, bacon and eggs. Elfrieda was on a course in London for a week studying feminist astrology.

Before becoming liberated, Elfrieda had hung onions and herbs from the beams and covered the dresser, tables and window sill with pot plants. The only life remaining now was in the mould which covered the few brown vestiges of these once-vigorous plants, while spiders draped their shrouds, funereal with smoke and dust, from every projection.

Having peeled off his thick woollen socks and hung them on

the chromium-plated bar running along the front of the Aga, Ivor was sitting barefoot at the kitchen table reading the *Guardian*. 'Kelvin? He asked himself round? How odd! Perhaps he's worried about this poaching thing and wants our advice.'

'Perhaps.'

A chorus of chicken squawks overtured the cacophonic timpani of Kelvin's Land Rover. A few seconds later, the door from the yard into the kitchen crashed open and Kelvin entered, removing his boots and coat and tossing them into a corner.

The commander and Ivor looked at him curiously. 'You look like a man with something on his mind, Kelvin,' said Ivor.

Kelvin's brow furrowed and he looked uneasily from one to the other.

'Was it something to do with this morning's activities?' prompted the commander.

Kelvin sighed like a seal at a blow-hole before taking the plunge. 'If I told you something, would you promise to keep it to yourselves? Just between the three of us?'

The commander stopped pottering round with a frying pan and sat down at the table with the others, his eyes gleaming. 'Kelvin, I would respect your secrets just as you would respect mine.'

'Huh!' snorted Kelvin. 'You're going to have to do better than that!'

'All right. On my honour, I won't say a thing.'

Kelvin peered suspiciously round the kitchen but there were no obvious listening devices. He hitched his chair closer to the table and they all leaned forward. 'That goose I shot,' he whispered hoarsely. 'I need a bit of help with it, especially since Percy wants it kept as evidence.'

The commander and Ivor looked at each blankly. 'So?'

'It's really very embarrassing and I don't know how it happened.'

'How what happened?' asked the commander patiently.

'How I came to shoot it.'

Looking baffled, the commander leaned back in his chair. 'I suppose you shot it because that's what we were there for. Good shot, too, I'd have thought. It's a pity about the gamekeeper, but Percy seems to know what it's all about and I don't think

195

there'll be any serious trouble. I shouldn't worry too much about the goose.'

'You don't understand.'

'How the hell can I be expected to understand if you won't tell us what this is all about? What's the big mystery?'

Kelvin sighed once more. 'When I got over the hedge I saw the goose. And do you know what? It wasn't a goose at all.'

'What was it?' asked Ivor. 'A bloody angel?'

'It might as well have been.' He jerked his thumb over his shoulder. 'I've got a dead swan out there in the Land Rover!'

'What? A swan!' exclaimed the commander. 'Good grief! That's dreadful!'

'Don't you dare!' said Kelvin, in response to the beginnings of a giggle from Ivor. 'It's no laughing matter. If you shoot a swan, they can fine you thousands, confiscate your car and throw you in jail. Even Percy wouldn't have been able to help if that Baldwick had seen it. When I saw what it was, I covered it in mud so that the feathers wouldn't show through.'

'But what on earth did you go and shoot it for in the first place?' demanded the commander. 'You can't do that. Swans belong to the Queen.'

'I didn't mean to, you fool! It was just that I'd been hearing Bill rabbiting on about whistling and honking and I'd been telling everyone to keep their heads under the hedge so I just upped and fired without really thinking about it. I mean, you wouldn't think of a swan flying over, now would you? Especially when it was so dark. Then Percy and what's-his-name turned up before I could pick it up.'

Ivor wiped his eyes and blew his nose on a red-spotted handkerchief. 'Oh, how lovely. What kind of swan is it?'

'It's a whooper swan.'

'Why did you tell us, Kelvin? I'm delighted that you did as it's brightened up a rather miserable morning, so far. But it's not like you to let this out.'

'It's just that Percy's going to be round looking for that goose for evidence.'

'So? Why didn't you just bury it rather than tell us all about it?'

'Yes! Good point, Ivor,' said the commander. 'Why?'

'Well, I was going to bury it and tell Percy the dog had stolen it. But then I thought what a waste it would be. I mean, it's not every day you get a swan. I haven't eaten a swan since I was a lad and I'm not likely to get the opportunity too often again. I thought you might cook it, Commander, being as how you're interested in things like that since Elfrieda became a suffragette.'

'Heavens!' murmured Ivor. 'What a remarkable idea!'

'Cook a swan! It's not an opportunity that comes to a chap that often,' agreed the commander thoughtfully. 'I think we may have a deal, Kelvin, so long as you clear things up with Percy. It really would be rather fun. Swans used to be served at royal banquets, you know. Like peacocks.'

'Yes! And larks' tongues!' added Ivor with a gourmet's glint in his eye.

'Huh!' grunted Kelvin, 'Larks' tongues! I know all about larks' tongues. Like rubber bands, they are. I used to catch larks with lime when I was a nipper and flog the tongues to the vicar for a farthing. Gave him terrible trouble, they did. Always getting jammed up in his teeth. Nasty gristly little things, larks' tongues.' Kelvin waggled his teeth in reminiscent disgust.

The other two were silent as they conjured up pictures of the culinary pearls cast before the piglet Kelvin.

'How would you cook a swan? I mean, it's probably not even in Mrs Beeton,' said Ivor.

'Roast it like a turkey,' said the commander, 'with a bit of sage.'

'You'll do it, then?' asked Kelvin.

'Yes,' said the commander incisively. 'As you've eaten swan before, Kelvin, how long do you think it should hang for?'

'Depends how old it is. But it's not the sort of thing to have hanging up in a shed for a couple of weeks. Someone might see it.'

'Yes, I suppose you're right. I think if you bring it in, we'll pluck it straight away. I could serve it this evening.'

'I've got a couple of bottles of Lafite that I've been saving for a special occasion,' said Ivor.

'Bring them along then. Kelvin, why don't you get in the bird?'

'Right. I'll do that.'

Putting on his boots, Kelvin disappeared out through the kitchen door. He returned, grunting with effort, bearing a blue plastic fertilizer bag and tipped it out on to the kitchen table. The contents slithered out on to the pine surface, filling the room with the powerful swampy smell of peat bog.

'It's very big, but are you sure it's a swan?' asked Ivor.

'Yes,' replied Kelvin. 'It certainly used to be one, anyway.'

The mud coating the bird was yellow and thick, hiding its contours as well as its plumage. Kelvin delicately peeled away a large gobbet which enveloped the head and beak.

'See? If it was a Canada goose, the beak would be black. This has got a yellow one, half yellow anyway. I was lucky to get one of these, they're rare in this part of the world. I've only shot mute swans before.'

'Hmm,' said the commander. 'I suggest you take it outside and rinse it under the tap in the yard.'

Kelvin disappeared for a couple of minutes, giving the commander time to clear away the mud and cover the table with newspaper. The bird with which Kelvin returned was undeniably a swan. He placed it on its back on the table, its head and neck hanging over the edge.

'It's got a ring on its leg,' said Ivor. 'You ought to send it back, Kelvin. You could say it flew into a power line.'

'Will they pay for the stamp?'

'I'm sure they will,' replied the commander reassuringly. 'It looks awfully big. We'd better pluck it now, because it's going to need a long time in the oven.'

It took him over an hour. The resultant carcass, the size of a substantial turkey, made their eyes gleam as it lay on the table surrounded by a snowstorm of feathers and down. The commander eviscerated and decapitated it with practised ease and laid it in a gargantuan roasting pan. He covered the breast with bacon and stuffed it into the oven of his Aga.

'That thing is going to be able to feed the Five Thousand, not just the three of us. We ought to give a party.' He rinsed his hands in the sink. 'Let's clear up the mess and then have some breakfast.'

'It's your mess,' replied Kelvin.

The commander's retort was interrupted by a knock at the door.

'Ah!' said Kelvin. 'You clear up and I'll see who's there.' He rose from his chair and padded over to open the door.

It was Percy.

Taking off his cap as he came through the kitchen door, Percy smiled amiably.

'Good morning again, gents,' he said. 'I was just on my way past and I saw your Land Rover, Kelvin. So I thought I'd save you trouble and pick up that goose.' He glanced past Kelvin to the others. 'If you don't mind, Commander.' He stepped forward with concern. 'Commander, are you all right? You've gone a funny colour. It's not wise to stand around in drizzle that early in the morning if you're not used to it. You may have caught a bit of a chill.' His eyes drifted towards the kitchen table and stopped.

The draft from the door had caught the drifts of swansdown and was tumbling it off the edge of the table in a slow avalanche.

'Blimey!' he said, stepping past Kelvin. 'It looks like a disaster.' He peered more closely at the table, at the floor and the window sills. Swansdown was everywhere. 'It's feathers. Wet feathers. What the hell's happened here?' He looked at Ivor.

Ivor turned his head hurriedly towards the commander. Percy's mildly enquiring eyes followed.

'Er . . .' said the commander, turning an even funnier colour. 'Er . . . I was putting some pillows through the washing machine and they burst. I was trying to dry off the feathers.'

'Oh, very good!' exclaimed Ivor involuntarily.

'Very good?' said Percy with a disapproving frown. 'I don't see what's so good about that. I think it's a very unfortunate accident.'

'That's just bloody silly,' said Kelvin.

'What's bloody silly?' asked the commander, his moustache flattening against his lips as they tightened.

'I ask you. Saying you put a pillow into your washing machine! That would be a pretty daft thing to do, even for you!'

'What other possible explanation could there be for having one's kitchen covered in wet swansdown, Kelvin?' asked the commander coldly.

'Well . . . er . . .'

'No, it's just bad luck, if you ask me,' said Percy, 'although you shouldn't buy such cheap pillows, Commander. Never stint on the quality of your pillow, I always say. Not if you want a good night's sleep.'

'What's wrong with my pillows?' asked the commander even more coldly.

'It's not really best-quality swansdown, is it?' asked Percy, picking up a feather that would have made a serviceable quill pen. 'I mean, if your Elfrieda gets one of these rammed into her earhole every night, it's not surprising she spends so much time away from home.'

'Constable, I would thank you not to tittle-tattle about my private affairs,' said the commander severely.

'I'm sorry, sir,' Percy apologized, stricken that he had allowed himself to slip out of his official persona.

'I should hope so, too.'

There was a pause.

'Yes,' said Percy, looking regretfully at the kettle bubbling on the stove and the bacon laid out ready for the frying pan. 'I suppose I'd better be getting on my way then. Kelvin, can I have your goose?'

'Yes, Kelvin,' said the commander, in whom the milk of human kindness had curdled. 'Give him the goose.'

'Ah! The goose! Yes. Well, I haven't got it with me.'

'Bloody silly,' said the commander acidly. 'Where is it?'

'You leave the questions to Percy here,' said Kelvin with alarm.

'Thank you,' said Percy. 'Where is the goose?'

'I've forgotten,' he said sullenly.

'You've forgotten!'

The derision of Ivor and the commander was more than Kelvin could bear.

'No, I haven't! I remember now. I left it in the Land Rover when I went to put away my gun and the dog ate it.'

The other three considered the explanation. 'Thin, Kelvin, very thin,' commented the commander.

'Thick enough for Percy, though, ain't it?'

It wasn't.

'You're pissing me about, Kelvin. No dog would eat a whole raw goose. Look, it's in your own interests. That Baldwick is trying to make it as difficult as possible and I'm trying to quieten things down. Everyone saw you'd shot that goose and there's no bloody point in hiding it. It'll just get Baldwick more riled and I'd have a bloody good mind to get riled at you too! So where's the goose?'

'Yes,' said the commander with a sweet smile, 'where's the goose?'

'Honestly, Percy, I have lost it.'

'That won't be good enough. You're just going to have to find it again. You can bring it round to the station later on this morning. You're a silly bugger, Kelvin Morchard, and you always have been!'

Nodding a farewell to Ivor and the commander, Percy replaced his cap and stumped out of the house.

Kelvin turned savagely towards the commander as the door shut. 'You bastard! You might at least have backed me up!'

'It's your own fault,' said Ivor. 'You did your best to drop him in it. You're lucky he didn't make things much more awkward for you.'

'You're a bastard too!' exclaimed Kelvin. 'What am I going to do?'

'I'm sure you'll think of something,' said the commander.

'Bastards!' exclaimed Kelvin once more. He looked round the kitchen in frustration. 'I'll be back this evening at 7 to eat that swan. Mind you cook it properly!'

When the commander arrived at the Hunted Hind at lunchtime, the bar was empty. Hanging his coat on the row of pegs by the door, he went behind the bar to pour himself a barley wine. He took a long pull before walking round to perch on one of the stools. Wiping his moustache, he focused his eyes comfortably on the lifeboat beside the till.

Five minutes later the latch clicked and the hinges creaked open on another customer. The commander swivelled on the stool, his corduroys farting against its thinly padded plastic top.

A worried frown preceded Percy through the door. It cleared when it saw the commander.

'Ah! I thought I might find you in here.'

'Did you?' replied the commander, not entirely happy about the implications of the remark. 'Did you come in for a drink, or did you want to see me about something?'

'Well, I don't mind if I do.'

'Thank you, I'll have another barley wine.'

They looked at each other like grand masters realizing that stalemate was the inevitable outcome of their game. Percy shrugged, going behind the bar to pour himself a pint of beer.

'What is it you want?' asked the commander.

'I've just had Kelvin round with his goose.'

'Heavens!'

Percy gave a sour grimace. 'I should have known better than to let the damn thing out of my sight in the first place. Tell me, did you see it after Kelvin shot it?'

'Why?'

Percy sighed. 'Why? It's a perfectly simple question. Can't you just give me a simple answer?'

The commander thought for a few seconds. 'Yes. I did see the goose. So did you and everybody else. What about it?'

'Could you identify its species?'

The commander was on safer ground here. 'Certainly not. I saw him carry a mud-covered object back to his car. But I've no idea what it was. Is there some sort of problem?'

'I've got Baldwick on my back.'

'Yes, but I don't quite understand what you're going on about the . . . er . . . goose for.'

'Kelvin turned up with one of his own geese, a farmyard goose, and says that was what he shot.'

'Gosh!' said the commander reverently.

'It makes a nonsense of the poaching charge. You can't poach your own goose. He hadn't even got the grace to shoot the bloody bird. He'd wrung its neck. Says that he had only blanks in his gun and the bird got such a fright that it crashed and broke its neck.'

'Into a bog?'

'He's just covering himself,' said Percy bitterly. 'Quite apart from poaching, he's making sure he can't be got for armed trespass. He says his cousin gave him permission to go for a walk and the last thing he intended to do was shoot anything which is why he had blanks.'

'Can farmyard geese fly?' asked the commander, probing delicately for areas of weakness.

'It's a bit difficult to prove otherwise when it's dead. Baldwick's doing his nut. I don't mind that, but Kelvin has no right to make me look a fool.'

'That's nothing to do with him,' reassured the commander. 'What have you done with the . . . er . . . evidence?'

'That's another reason I wanted to see you. There was no point in holding on to the goose, so he took it back. He said that he was going to ask you to cook it and he invited me round to your place this evening to eat it. It seemed a bit of a liberty, so I thought I'd like to check that it was all right.'

The commander smiled.

'Fine, so long as you bring some booze, Percy. Swan up about 7.30.'

Chapter Ten

Birth

STAMPING HIS feet to shake the snow from his boots, Bill came into the Hunted Hind. 'If there isn't a change in the next twelve hours, I reckon we ought to go to the sale,' he said.

An east wind sliced down from the moor through the leafless trees and hedges, edging the river under the bridge with ice. The streets of Moorcombe were deserted. The pub, bedecked with tinsel and baubles for Christmas, still a fortnight away, was crowded. The low murmur of conversation was punctuated by the thud of darts, although the players were scarcely discernible through the tobacco haze.

'What sale?' asked Mandy, who was not grafted on to the agricultural grapevine.

'Chap called Davidson, out beyond the five-cross way. It's amazing he survived this long.'

'Why?'

'He's stupid, that's why,' said Annie. 'He came down here six years ago and thought he was still upcountry. Bought lots of machinery. Bit of drought, bit of flood, a few snow drifts and he's bust. It could be a decent sale.'

'Yes,' said Bill. 'At this time of year, even without this weather, there'd be few enough people going. Now, with the snow, there'll be some real bargains about.'

'Why are you telling us all this?' asked Kelvin suspiciously.

'I need someone to bid for me. The auction's being run by Desmond Pile and I've had the better of him too often. If he sees me bidding, he'll run me up. I thought you might like to come along.'

'I'll come,' said the commander. 'I bought a couple of sows off him a few years back. He thinks I'm an idiot.'

'I remember those pigs,' said Kelvin. 'One had only eight teats and the other ate her first litter. Yes, you're the man to make the bids. But I'm coming too. I'll bring the Land Rover.'

'In that case you can give us a lift. If the snow doesn't go away, we'll need four-wheel drive. You can pick me up at 11.'

'Me too,' said Mandy.

'I'll charge for petrol.'

'We'll buy you a drink,' said the commander.

'That'll do. Make it a whisky,' said Kelvin. 'Right now.'

The following morning the sky was leaden and the wind swept the thin sheets of snow from the fields, depositing it in shallow drifts where gateways split the hedgebanks.

The Land Rover rumbled out of the village, heading up the river towards the moor. Inside Prudence sat in front beside Kelvin, while Bill, Mandy and the commander were squeezed in the back.

'Did you hear the forecast?' asked Bill.

'What?' said Kelvin. His vehicle had an exhaust which trumpeted its approach. It also squeaked, rattled and groaned.

'I asked whether you'd heard the forecast!' roared Bill. 'There's snow coming later. We'd better make sure we don't get stuck away from home.'

'They were frightened to send the milk tankers down to the farms this morning,' contributed Kelvin, sawing at the steering wheel, which had to be moved through an arc of 90 degrees before his intention was translated through to the wheels. 'We had to take our milk to the emergency collection point. But it doesn't feel like proper snow to me. Too cold. Whoops!'

The vehicle slewed across the road, Kelvin jammed on the brakes and leapt out.

'What are you doing?' asked the commander.

'Hang on a minute!'

In the hedge an arrow-shaped sign inscribed 'Sale This Day' pointed down a side road. Kelvin turned it to point in the opposite direction, stood back to admire his handiwork and returned to the Land Rover. His boots left tracks in the snow.

'Good thinking, Kelvin,' said Bill approvingly.

The sale lay 5 miles and three more signs further away from Moorcombe and when they arrived they were greeted by a gratifying paucity of vehicles.

After a brief look at the lots on offer, they rendezvous-ed in the barn, where the auctioneer's office was sited.

'Morning, Kelvin,' said the clerk, a man in his fifties with white hair and broken veins on his cheeks.

'Morning, Willie. How's the wife?'

'In hospital.'

'Are you having to do your own cooking?'

'Yes.'

'Bad luck! Are there any reserves on the lots?'

'No.'

Kelvin smiled. 'We ought to do all right then.'

'You'll do all right but all the decent stuff's been re-possessed.' The clerk looked at the others. 'Hullo, Bill. Pile's going to give you a hard time.' The commander, having been in the area for only five years, merited merely a nod. The clerk looked at Prudence, his eyes widening. 'Bloody hell, Prudence! What's wrong with you?'

'I'm pregnant,' replied Prudence.

'I didn't hear you'd got yourself married!'

'I haven't.'

'Oh.' The clerk cast a sideways glance at Kelvin.

'Don't look at me like that,' scowled the grandfather-to-be. 'This sort of thing's quite normal these days. Anyway, it was Prudence who wouldn't get married. Not the bloke.'

'Who is the bloke?'

'Archie Spontini.'

'Joy's son? I'd heard he was back. Takes after his father, does he? He was meant to have been a randy bugger.'

'It was my choice to have a baby,' said Prudence.

'Oh quite,' agreed the clerk. 'When's it due?'

'Just after Christmas. We're going to call him Brett.'

'That's very nice,' said Willie, his voice carefully neutral. 'Who's going to do the milking, Kelvin?'

'I'll do it myself. It'll only be for a couple of days.'

'Excuse me.' Looking at his watch, Willie picked up a brass hand bell, rose to his feet and went to the open door. There he clanged the bell loudly for a full ten seconds before returning to his desk.

'Not very nice out there,' he said. 'Wouldn't surprise me if there was a bit more snow.'

'Too chilly,' said Kelvin, leading his party out into the field behind the barn, where the lots were laid out.

The wind was bitingly cold, blowing gritty flakes of snow against the hedge and amongst the sheets of corrugated iron, drinking bowls, tools and other oddments. There were fifteen people clustered round the wooden box that served as the rostrum where Desmond Pile, a small thin man in his early forties, swamped by a sheepskin coat, stood with a large umbrella at his back to shield him from the worst of the weather. He waited until Kelvin and the others had gathered round.

'Right, gentlemen. It's not a very nice day, so I would ask you to bid up and we can get this over as soon as possible. The usual conditions of sale apply and I would emphasize that all lots are to be sold without reserve.' He looked down at his assistant, who fumbled with a pen and clipboard in mittened hands. 'Right?' called Pile. He received a nod in reply. 'Gentlemen, Lot 1. A chain harrow. Who will bid me £20?'

The chain harrow, like all chain harrows, had half its links missing and, like most chain harrows, failed to attract a bid. The dung spreader went for £50. The five lots of assorted tools, each salted with a couple of horse brasses, were bought by two middle-aged ladies with an antiques stall. The tractor, red, rusty, bald-tyred, failed to start, thereby attracting no bids. The commander, with Bill as his puppet master, bought steadily, picking up rolls of barbed wire, fence posts, stacks of timber and a fertilizer spinner.

By early afternoon, the temperature drove Mandy, Prudence and Kelvin back into the barn, where the clerk had a 10 kw electric heater blowing hot air at his feet. Leaning over the desk, he was picking his teeth, the local paper opened before him at the funeral reports. He looked up as everyone came in.

'I thought you'd've gone to Peter Clapp's funeral, Kelvin.'

'I did.'

'Well, they haven't listed your name among the mourners.'

'What?' Kelvin bent over the desk and peered down at the newsprint. 'Bugger it! I haven't got my glasses. Prudence, check it for me, will you? I was representing Ivor as well. If they've missed us out, they'll have to put in an apology next week.'

'Is there a lavatory here?' asked Prudence.

'Lean-to by the house,' said Willie.

'Here! Hang on a minute!' said her father. 'Look through these names first.'

But Prudence was already on her way. 'I'll just be a minute, Dad. It's the cold. Have Mandy read it to you.'

'Women!' snorted Kelvin.

'Be fair, Kelvin,' said Mandy. 'Men don't get pregnant.'

'True, but men've got better control. Anyway, check if Willie's right about the paper, will you?'

Willie was right about the paper. Meanwhile, outside, the sale went on. By mid-afternoon, Bill and the commander had had enough. They retreated to the barn, blue in the face and shuddering with cold.

'Bloody hell!' said Bill. 'That's it for me. He could be could give the rest away, but I still wouldn't stick it!'

'Shall we settle up, then?' said the commander, stamping his feet.

'About bloody time,' said Kelvin. 'We'll warm up the Land Rover.'

Mandy and Kelvin turned up their coat collars and went out into the snow-filled dusk. A minute or two later, the others joined them.

'Just as well we're not staying to the end,' remarked Kelvin. 'The weather looks dirtier all the time. Glad I'm in this rather than the van.'

'Aye. The pub should be open when we get back. Anyone fancy a drink?' asked Bill. 'I've had a good afternoon.'

'That's very civil of you, Bill.' Kelvin crunched the lever into first gear and tracked his way across the yard.

'Stop!' screamed Mandy with such vehemence that Kelvin jammed on the brakes.

'Shit!' said Kelvin. 'What did you want to go and do that for?'

'We've forgotten Prudence.'

Kelvin looked over his shoulder to count heads. 'Bugger me! So we have. Pop back and get her, would you?'

'Go yourself!' replied Mandy.

'She might be back in the lavatory again. I can't go into a ladies'.'

'It's not a ladies', it's just a loo. Bang on the door.'

'She's pregnant. She might need a woman's help,' replied Kelvin. He had no intention of going out to face the weather, which now seemed to be working up to a blizzard.

'Idle bastard!' muttered Mandy as she opened the door. 'She's your bloody daughter, poor woman!'

The vehicle rocked on its springs as she slammed the door.

Kelvin adjusted the mirror. 'What are you going to do with the stuff you've bought, Bill?'

'Sell most of it on. I know where I can place that spreader already.'

Kelvin yawned, drumming his fingers on the steering wheel. The lights from the dashboard instruments glinted on his stubble.

'Have you got everything ready for the baby?' asked the commander.

'It's nothing to do with me,' responded Kelvin. 'But Prudence seems to have everything under control. Lindy made her go to birth classes on Tuesday afternoons. Buggered if I know why. Women don't need lessons. It happens whether they like it or not.' He yawned again. 'Archie's been quite good too. Her and he went out and bought a cot and put it the back bedroom.' He faced the others squarely and smiled. 'I got the lad a toy tractor at market last week. A John Deere, just like Ivor's. Bloody nearly cost as much, too.'

The passenger door flew open. A flurry of snow on a blast of cold air entered the cab.

'Get in and shut the bloody door,' said Kelvin. Mandy stood there, her mouth opening and shutting like one of the shubunkin in her garden pond. 'What the hell's wrong with you?'

'It's Prudence. She's having a baby.'

'I know. We've just been talking about it.'

'She's having it now.'

'No, she isn't. She's having it after Christmas.'

Under its thick layer of make-up Mandy's face had taken on a greenish tinge that could not have been explained by the cold.

'You silly bugger! She's having it now! In the loo!'

'Ohmygod!' said Bill. 'Prudence is calving early.'

Bill may have understood, but Kelvin was unwilling to believe that he was about to become a grandfather.

'Look, woman,' he said, exasperated. 'I should know. I'm the one who's got to take her in to the hospital. She's booked into the County General the day after Boxing Day.'

'You stupid old bastard!' cried Mandy. 'I'm telling you, she's in labour now. Her water's broken. She's having her baby in the loo.'

At last Kelvin twigged. 'Oh no, we'd better do something. Bill, call the vet, call the vet!'

'Shut up!' ordered Mandy. 'Pull yourself together. We've got to get her to hospital! Commander, come and help me.'

The commander did not argue. He may have been thinking coolly in a crisis, but more likely his service training responded to the note of authority in Mandy's voice. He slid out of the back door on to the inch of snow that now covered the yard.

'Is there a rug or something in there?' demanded Mandy.

'There are some sacks in the back,' replied Kelvin.

Bill handed them to the commander, who disappeared with Mandy into the gathering darkness.

'I'd back up across the yard, Kelvin. It'll be less of a walk for them.'

Kelvin backed obediently across the yard.

'Are you all right?' asked Bill.

'I don't know.' Kelvin hauled on the handbrake and punched the steering wheel with his fist. 'I'm going to be a grandfather. Christ! Me a grandfather!' He swivelled in the seat. 'Where are we going to put her? You come into the front, Bill, and the commander can squeeze in beside us. That'll leave Mandy and Prudence in the back. We should be able to get to the hospital in about forty-five minutes.'

The others arrived.

'Her contractions have started!' called Mandy, trotting alongside the commander who had Prudence leaning on his arm. 'I'll need hot water and towels!'

'Bugger that!' said Bill. 'We've got to get her to hospital. Are you all right, my dear?'

'I'm fine,' said Prudence, looking rather pale. 'I'm sorry about this. I thought I'd simply wet myself, but it's the baby. Seems he's decided to come early.'

'It's all right. You'll be there in a jiffy.' Bill patted her reassuringly.

'I pinched a rug from the auctioneers and they're going to phone through to the cottage hospital and tell them we're coming,' said the commander. He released Prudence's arm and Bill helped her into the back. Mandy made to follow her.

'No, I'd like Bill beside me, please,' said Prudence.

'Bill?' said Mandy. 'Don't be silly!'

'I want Bill. He's delivered a few thousand calves and lambs in his time. I doubt if I'll be much different.'

'But . . .'

'Don't argue, woman!' shouted Kelvin. 'Get in the front with the commander!'

Headlights on full beam, four-wheel drive engaged, the Land Rover roared out of the yard.

'Don't you shout at me like that, Kelvin,' Mandy said angrily. 'It's quite wrong that Bill should be in the back. I'm a woman. It should be me. Kelvin? Are you listening to me?' She dug the commander violently in the ribs. 'Move over and keep your elbows to yourself!'

'Shut up, Mandy, or I'll chuck you out,' said Kelvin.

Mandy took a deep breath but held her peace. Grunts came from the seat behind.

'What's going on back there?'

'Keep your eyes on the road, Dad. I'm just getting off my jeans. It's difficult to have a baby in jeans.'

'Are you going to be able to hold on?' asked Mandy, anxious.

'I think so.'

'She thinks so!' muttered Kelvin. 'She thinks so!'

'In a cow, you'd expect a wait of three quarters of an hour after the bag bursts,' said Bill thoughtfully.

'How long ago did it break, Prudence?' asked Mandy.

'Fifteen minutes, I suppose.'

'On the other hand,' Bill went on, 'if Prudence was a horse, you'd expect her to foal about twenty minutes after the waters. But with women I'm not sure what the time is.'

'Christ!' prayed Kelvin. 'Let her be a cow and not a horse!'

By now he had hit the main road and was rattling along at nearly 50 mph. The headlights trapped a cone of snow, and seemed to suck it in to scour the windscreen. The road was white, the roar of the tyres was muffled as arabesques of snow chased beneath the wheels.

'Aahh!' groaned Prudence.

'What's wrong?' asked the commander.

'It's a contraction, you fool!' said Mandy.

'I feel a bit queasy,' said the commander.

'Tough!' said Kelvin savagely.

'Would it be possible to drop me off at the turn-off to Moorcombe? I could walk home from there.'

'It's a mile. You'd be a fool to try it in this weather,' said Bill.

'If I stay here, I'm afraid I might be sick.'

Kelvin jammed on the brakes. The vehicle, obeying the laws of physics as dictated by its speed, the road conditions and the fact that the only fully functioning brake was on the nearside front wheel, pirouetted twice and ricocheted off a tree.

'Get out!'

'Can't you take me on a bit?' asked the commander. 'It's still a quarter of a mile to the turning.'

'Get out!' shouted Kelvin. 'I haven't got time to piss about!'
Another groan from Prudence underlined his point.

'Yes,' said the commander. 'I'm sorry about this. I don't
know what came over me.' He buttoned up his coat, turned up
his collar and pulled the door handle. 'Er . . . good luck,
Prudence. I'm sorry, but this sort of thing has always made me
feel a bit funny.'

'Aah!' replied Prudence.

'Out!' repeated Kelvin.

'The door appears to be stuck,' the commander said
nervously. 'It must have been the tree.'

Mandy leaned across the commander and thumped the door with the heel of her hand. It flew open and the commander toppled out on to the snow. 'Right! Let's go!'

They went.

Swooping into a roundabout, the Land Rover turned towards the cottage hospital. They were in the next town, 10 miles from Moorcombe. It was rush hour. Kelvin roared through the narrow streets, his defective exhaust racketing between the buildings.

'Out of the bloody way!' Kelvin yelled, cutting through a gap left by the secretary to the financial manager of the agricultural co-operative and a middle-aged woman who worked in the Oxfam shop on Thursday afternoons.

The secretary braked to avoid collision and a British Telecom van slid into her boot. Two other vehicles slid into him, but Kelvin was gone, rattling the wrong way up a narrow alley. Two minutes later the Land Rover burst into the hospital courtyard.

'Bloody hell, what a trip!' said Bill, easing himself out of the Land Rover after Mandy and Prudence, accompanied by a nurse, had disappeared up the steps into the hospital. 'Another five minutes and we'd have been too late!'

'I thought so. Prudence was born in a hurry too. Her mother was supposed to have gone out to collect the eggs. Instead, she dropped Prudence in the henhouse.'

'I remember that.'

'I had to get the eggs later myself.'

'Children make extra work for everybody.'

Kelvin snorted. 'I'm going to try and make sure this one doesn't. D'y think we should go in?'

'We'll have to.'

They climbed up the steps, orange from the neon lights that reflected on the snow. Going through the entrance, they were faced by a long linoleum-covered corridor. It was deserted. Kelvin tried the door to what seemed an office. At that moment a nurse came round a corner.

'What are you two doing?' she asked.

'I'm looking for my Prudence. She's having a baby.'

'Well, you've come to the wrong hospital. We don't do

214

maternity here. We're mainly geriatric. You should be at the County General.'

'We brought her here five minutes ago,' said Bill. 'She was having a baby, all right.'

'Really?' The nurse seemed sceptical. 'I would suggest you go up to the waiting room, then, and you'll be told if there's any news.' She pointed along the corridor. 'Turn left at the end and it's the second door on the right.'

'Thank you, miss,' said Kelvin.

She stared suspiciously after them as they walked down the corridor, their gumboots clumping on the polished floor. Kelvin looked over his shoulder at her and gave a little wave.

'Horrid smell, hospitals,' said Bill. 'Just like one of Frank Mattock's pig sties. They must use the same kind of disinfectant.'

'Just the thing for a cold night, that nurse,' remarked Kelvin, a gleam in his eye.

In the waiting room Mandy was sitting in a threadbare armchair reading a copy of *Country Life*.

'What's happening?' asked Kelvin.

Mandy shrugged. 'I don't know. They told me to wait in here.'

Kelvin looked round the room. 'It's not like it is on the telly. I thought the waiting room would have rows of chairs and lots of drunks with bleeding heads and things.'

'That's the late night shift in a casualty department. You wouldn't expect anyone to be waiting here at this time of night.'

Kelvin sniffed. 'You'd think there might at least be someone waiting for their granny to snuff it. Though I suppose if they're that oven-ready, they'd be past changing their wills anyway.'

A small young nurse put her head round the door. 'Is one of you the father?'

'That's me,' said Kelvin.

The nurse wrinkled her lip. 'A bit old, ain't'ya?'

'Old? Don't you be cheeky, girl! I'm in the prime of life.'

'All right, dear. I didn't mean nothing. Anyway, come with me.'

Kelvin followed her through the door. 'Where are we going?'

'To help Mother. She'll be needing lots of support.'

'Help Mother? That's not my job, it's yours. That's why we brought Prudence here.'

'I'm just doing what sister said,' said the nurse over her shoulder as she scampered up a flight of stairs. Kelvin followed with trepidation. She pushed through some swing doors. 'I've got the father, Sister,' she said.

'He's only just in time.'

Prudence, practically naked, lay on a bed with her legs in the air. A nurse was seated at the end of the mattress with a cup of tea in her hand. A second nurse sat by the patient, patting her hand.

The patting nurse looked up with a smile. 'Isn't this exciting? I haven't seen a baby born since my midwifery course.' Indicating a brace of large gas cylinders by the bed, she asked, 'Does anyone here know how to work these things?'

Kelvin was aghast. 'What have you brought me here for? This is disgusting!'

'Disgusting?'

'Yes, this is no place for a man. Nobody should see his daughter like this. Cover yourself, Prudence!'

Prudence was thinking about matters other than decorum. Thrashing her head from side to side, she groaned.

The nurse with the tea looked suddenly grim. 'Daughter! This woman's your daughter as well?'

'Yes. That's Prudence Morchard. I'm Kelvin Morchard.'

'You revolting old man! You ought to be put in jail!'

'Nurse!' The voice from the other end of the bed rang out with authority. 'We'll discuss this later.'

'Sorry, Sister,' replied her colleague. 'It's just that incest makes my blood boil.'

'How dare you!' shouted Kelvin.

Just then Prudence let out a mighty cry.

'Oh look!' said sister. 'The baby's coming! That's its head. Isn't she quick!'

Kelvin looked. He saw. He was vaguely aware of the gurgles of the delighted nurses as his senses took leave of him. Toppling forward like a tree, nose first, he hit the anaesthetic cylinders and then the floor. Round his head, like a satanic halo, a pool of blood spread from his nose.

His downfall brought about the downfall of the tanks, which

in turn crashed to the floor, bouncing against a central heating radiator before coming to rest across sister's foot.

The latter broke, as did the former, which vented a jet of scalding water up to the ceiling. There were shrieks from sister, pained by her broken foot, cries from the two other nurses, showered by boiling water, and uproar as a thundering herd of hospital staff flocked to their rescue.

In the midst of the confusion Kelvin lay blissfully unconscious alongside Prudence's bed. She, as always, got on with her business and all by herself brought forth Brett.

On Christmas Eve, the day of Brett's christening, the weather was back to normal. A sullen drizzle leaked from a leaden cloud that cowered in the valley to escape the gale roaring across the barren moor above.

The church had been decorated by the primary school children. The infant Jesus, his face carved from a Pentland Crown potato donated by Jimmy, lay in his cradle beneath the shiny black marble of the Victorian font.

Mr Richard Alworthy, the new vicar, a born-again currency speculator formerly of Cannon Street and now serving six moorland parishes, greeted the invited guests in the porch with a smile and a tiny bow which bordered on a curtsy. At first he had refused, but when Archie crumpled a £20 note into his damp palm, the vicar had overcome his doubts about the chosen hymn *Unto Us a Child is Born*.

Kelvin and the squire, soon to be godfather, sat in the front row beside Prudence and Archie. Behind them the public bar of the Hunted Hind filled ten rows. Bill and Jimmy in unaccustomed suits and ties fidgeted uneasily on the ancient oak pews. Next to them, Mandy fiercely nudged Ivor who was paring his fingernails.

As the reedy mumble of a congregation in full throat stole down the tunnels bored in the roof beams by dozing battalions of death watch beetle, Kelvin was seen to steal a glance at his bawling grandchild. Down his cheek as far as the bandage which swaddled his nose ran a viscous tear.

As the vicar wrestled to take the child from Prudence so that he could splash it 'Brett', it stopped crying. A peevish expression crossed its face.

In the third pew Father Loosemire gave a start of recognition. The celebratory drinks and the emotion of the occasion, together with the family resemblance between the baby and its grandmother that last time the postman had seen her, brought a lump to his throat and despite himself he wept for Joy.